Vacation at Sunshine Farm

Summer #1— A Bumpy Ride

Andrea Wandel

Summer #1— A Bumpy Ride

Translated by Karen Nickel Anhalt

Copyright: © Andrea Wandel 2009
Original title: Ferien auf dem Sonnenhof
Cover and inside illustrations: Eleonore Gerhaher
Cover layout: © Stabenfeldt A/S
Typeset by Roberta L. Melzl
Editor: Bobbie Chase
Printed in Germany, 2009

Stabenfeldt, Inc.
457 North Main Street
Danbury, CT 06811
www.pony4kids.com

ISBN: 978-1-934983-02-7

Available exclusively through PONY.

Horseback riding camp in idyllic Upper Marlboro for boys and girls, 8-16 years of age. Affectionate care, exceptionally beautiful grounds for trail rides and riding instructions with well-trained ponies and horses guaranteed. Lodgings in our picturesque farmhouse. All guests will have their own horse or pony to care for. Contact: Marty Sunshyne, sunshine@horsemail. com <mailto:sonnenschein@horsemail.de>, Tel. ...

Chapter 1

"Vacation at Sunshine Farm?"

June put down the magazine and glared at her mother.

"What's that supposed to mean?"

"What do you think?"

Martha Sunshyne (or Marty as she was known) blew a strand of fiery red hair out of her face and sat down with her daughter June at the kitchen table.

"It's an advertisement. How do you like it?"

"An advertisement?" June frowned. "What for?"

"Sometimes I ask myself what you're going to school for when you don't understand the simplest things," sighed Marty as she poured herself a glass of orange juice. "For a riding camp, of course. Here with us. At Sunshine Farm. *Comprendes*?"

June reached for the magazine again.

"Romantic farmhouse? Where's that supposed to be?"

"Well," Marty pushed the glass away from herself and grinned sheepishly, "we do need to do a little work on the house."

"'A little work.' *That's* rich," mumbled June and

glanced out the window at the adjoining farm buildings. They could definitely stand a fresh coat of paint.

When her parents separated a year ago, she and her mother moved out here. A horse farm had always been Marty Sunshyne's great dream. But unfortunately, managing one wasn't quite as easy as she thought it would be. They could barely cover their operating expenses with the fees they took in for the few horses that were boarded there. And money was still tight occasionally. In that respect her mother was right – they did need a new idea. But was Marty Sunshyne, of all people, the right person to take on this venture? It's true that she was an excellent rider and riding instructor, but June wasn't too sure about her abilities as a businesswoman.

"And what do you mean by 'well-trained ponies and horses'?" June looked at her mother with an expression of alarm on her face. "You don't mean Nelson, do you?"

June would never give up her beloved Anglo-Arabian gelding for this crazy idea!

"Don't worry," Marty grinned. "You don't really believe that I'd be willing to listen to your complaining the whole time, do you? I have enough to deal with as it is."

"Well then what do you mean?" June was flabbergasted. "You can hardly start up a riding camp with Modena alone."

Modena was a pitch-black Oldenburg mare that her mother successfully rode in jumping competitions a few years ago. These days, however, the mare was 18 and enjoyed retired life on the sprawling paddocks of Sunshine Farm.

"I suppose we could let someone ride Modena every

so often," said Marty. "But one horse is obviously not enough, so…"

"So?" asked June.

"So I've been looking around for a few new horses."

"New horses?" June nearly gagged. "What are we supposed to buy them with?"

"Oh, you don't need to worry about that." Marty beamed at June. "Didn't you read those articles about the Haflingers that end up in the slaughterhouse?"

June thought for a moment. *Ah yes.* In the same magazine that her mother's advertisement ran in, there was an article a few weeks ago about Haflingers that were bred for the slaughterhouse.

"But the article was about foals. How long do you want to wait until they're trained and ready for you to give riding lessons on?"

"Well, obviously we can't use foals. The horses come from an organization that rescues foals and later sells them. Our five are five-year-olds that they haven't been able to place yet."

"*Our* five?" June shook her head. "You already bought them?"

"Of course," Marty laughed and got up. "We have to get started sometime. We've only got two months until summer vacation, you know. And in the meantime, you and I have a lot of work to do."

Work. Whenever her mother used that word, alarm bells went off in June's head. "Work with what?"

"With the Haflingers, of course. They still have to be trained."

"Trained," June repeated slowly. "What can they do?"

"Not that much. Well, actually…" Marty stammered

a little before finishing her sentence. "Actually, they're more or less unbroken."

"Unbroken? At age five?"

"Well, apparently they have been a little difficult. As I said, up till now they couldn't be placed. But don't worry, we can handle that. Besides, they were real cheap. You can see for yourself later. They're being delivered this afternoon."

June gaped at her mother.

"And you really think this is going to work, huh?"

"Sure do," said Marty authoritatively and noisily flung the dirty dishes into the dishwasher. "You'll see soon enough – this is THE idea."

A short time later, June stood on the large, graveled courtyard and then crossed to the open stable where Nelson and Modena were quartered. Curious, the black mare and the white gelding approached her. June attached the rope to Nelson's bridle and led him to the hitching post in front of the stable.

"Gosh, Nelson, you're not going go believe her latest idea," she said quietly and buried her face in Nelson's warm, strong neck. "A vacation camp. Here."

Nelson snorted quietly and turned his head to the side. June stepped back from him.

"Yes, you heard me right. A vacation camp. Here."

Shaking her head, she went into the saddle room in the building directly next to the open stable. A ride through the green meadows and golden fields that surrounded Sunshine Farm was exactly what she needed right now.

"Hey, June. How're you doing?"

June flinched, startled by the voice behind her. She turned around.

"Oh, Ben, it's you. You scared the daylights out of me."

"I believe you." Ben smiled broadly. "You seemed like you were totally lost in thought. What were you thinking about?"

Along with Maxi and Lena, Ben was one of June's best friends. He came by Sunshine Farm almost every day. Because he didn't have a horse of his own, he usually rode around on Björn, the Icelandic gelding. The chubby white horse was a sly old fellow. He belonged to Mrs. Hanson, who had two small children and couldn't get over to her horse all that often. That was why she was so happy that Ben took care of Björn.

"Would you like to go for a ride with me?"

June gave Ben a hopeful look.

"Sure. Then I'll tell you everything."

"Okey dokey." Ben grabbed Björn's snaffle and saddle and ran out to the courtyard. "I'll be ready in a minute."

Soon June and Ben were riding in step, reins loose, and they turned onto a path that led straight through the bright yellow canola fields.

"Isn't this gorgeous?" June sighed happily.

"Oh sure," said Ben. "But there was something you wanted to tell me, wasn't there?"

Curious, Ben directed Björn closer to Nelson and looked up at June.

"Exactly." June took a deep breath before telling Ben the whole story.

"A summer camp?" asked Ben when she finished. "Here?"

June nodded.

"Brilliant!" Ben exclaimed.

"You think so?"

June was not at all sure.

"Of course. Aren't you even happy about it?"

June thought for a moment. "Well, I guess it could be a lot of fun."

"Totally!" Ben exclaimed. "Bonfires, horse shows, long rides and who knows what else. Wow, June, things are finally going to happen around here. We're going to have a whole lot of fun!"

"And a whole lot of work," June sighed. "Just picture five nearly unbroken Haflingers that have to be trained in only two months. Not to mention the fact that I registered for jumping at the Zone 2 competition in Lakeville."

"And when is that?"

"In four weeks."

"Oh wow! That really does sound like a lot of work." Ben paused briefly, but then a huge smile spread across his face. "Oh come on. Nelson can do that in his sleep. And you can handle a few Haflingers. I'll help out, and I'm sure Lena and Maxi will give you a hand, too."

"You would really do that?"

June looked at him gratefully. There really was nothing better in the world than good friends! She motioned to the long dirt path ahead of them.

"What do you think? How about if we first let them trot a little and then gallop after we take the curve?"

"Okay," Ben said. "But don't let your Ferrari on four legs speed too much. Björn doesn't like to be left behind."

June laughed. Nelson was so fast that he left every horse at Sunshine Farm way behind him. And Ben's Icelandic would start to buck if the distance to the front horse got too great for him.

"I promise."

She trotted off and allowed Nelson to start galloping after the curve. The gelding snorted excitedly and she had to hold him back to prevent him from going too fast. Nelson loved to run more than anything else and couldn't comprehend why June wouldn't allow him to let loose. At the end of the path, she was completely out of breath because she had to work so hard to hold Nelson back. Even still, Ben and Björn were a good distance behind them.

"Whew." Ben pushed a dark brown lock of hair away from his face and smiled at June. "That was great. Do we want to go on or head back?"

"Nah, let's go back." June turned to ride in the direction they came from. "Who knows when the Haflingers are arriving. I'm sure my mom wants me to be there for that. And to be honest, I am just a teeny, tiny bit curious." June grinned, a little sheepishly.

Both kids held their reins loosely and rode back to Sunshine Farm in step with each other. Nelson tried to break into a trot, but with a few gentle moves and calming words, June managed to keep him in check.

"It's a good thing Mom doesn't want Nelson to be a school horse," said June shortly before they reached the farm. "Or we would have had a serious fight."

"I don't think that's something you have to worry about," Ben grinned. "Anyone can see that Nelson's much too sensitive. He'd go bananas with a bunch of different riders constantly sitting on his back."

"That's for sure." June stroked the silky soft coat on Nelson's neck. "A real Thoroughbred. I like it when horses are so delicate, then…"

She held her breath as they heard a loud rumbling coming from the direction of the farm.

"What's that noise?" asked Ben. "It sounds horrible."

"I'm afraid I know what it is."

June let Nelson go a little faster and rounded the corner of the farm. A large horse transporter was parked in front of the main building. The ramp was let down and Marty was just in the process of being jerked down it by a small but powerful chestnut with a long blonde mane. The chestnut whinnied shrilly and pulled so hard that Marty didn't have the slightest chance of controlling him. He dragged her along like a stuffed animal until the transport driver came to help her.

"Good grief," said Ben. "Are those the…"

"The well-trained horses for riding instruction, yeah," June finished the sentence. "Welcome to Sunshine Farm!"

Chapter 2

"Horseback riding camp in idyllic Upper Marlboro?"

Charly put down the magazine and glared at her mother.

"What's that supposed to mean?"

"What do you think?" Vanessa Schultz sat down on the edge of her daughter's bed. "Riding camp. It'll be just great."

"Just great?"

Charly threw the magazine on the floor and defiantly crossed her arms in front of her chest.

"I don't want to go there, do you understand? I – don't – want – to – go!"

"But sweetie, try to understand. I absolutely *have* to go on this business trip to London. Besides, riding is so nice. And once you see how much fun it is, well, who knows? Maybe Daddy will buy you your own horse."

"Daddy." Charly snorted contemptuously. "These days he'd buy me anything just to ease his guilty conscience."

"Charlotte!" Vanessa Schultz knelt down in front of the bed and laid her hands on Charly's shoulders. "Please don't say things like that. Your father can't help that we separated."

15

"Oh, I know, I know. A separation by mutual agreement," Charly mumbled darkly. "A clean break. Except that you totally forgot about your daughter." She looked at her mother accusingly.

"Oh sweetie, of course we didn't forget about you. But what were we supposed to do? Your father and I just grew apart. I know that it's not easy for you. It isn't easy for me either, but you'll see – we'll get used to it pretty quickly."

"You, maybe," said Charly, "but not me. Do you understand? Not me!"

"Charlotte…"

"No! Leave me alone! Just leave me alone!"

Charly threw herself on her bed and hugged her pillow to her face.

Her mother picked up the magazine wordlessly and lay it down on the small table next to the bed. Then she left the room. As the door closed behind her, Charly set the pillow aside and sat up. Alone at last.

Ever since her father moved out of the apartment two weeks ago, she had wanted to do nothing but stay in her room and hide from the world. Although her parents did fight a lot recently, she never would have thought that they would actually separate. Then her father packed his suitcases and moved to their big country house on the Potomac, where her family always used to spend their weekends together.

Used to.

Now everything was completely different.

Charly's gaze fell on the magazine near her bed. Lost in thought, she reached for it and read the advertisement again.

Affectionate care, exceptionally beautiful grounds for riding and riding instruction with well-trained ponies and horses guaranteed.

"Yuck." Charly shuddered. Ponies and horses. She had never understood what her mother found so appealing about those big, overgrown animals. Her mother even owned her own horse, a mare named Summer Dream. She boarded it at a large riding stable outside of Washington, DC, about a half hour away from their large four-bedroom house that Charly and her mother now lived in alone. Summer Dream was a birthday present from Charly's father. As a well-known management consultant, he could easily afford expensive gifts.

Charly had never been interested in Summer Dream, and to her mother's great disappointment, she only rarely accompanied her to the stable.

"But riding is so wonderful," Vanessa Schultz told her daughter again and again.

"You're out in the fresh air all day, have contact with animals, meet nice people," Charly quietly repeated what her mother told her all the time. *What a bunch of hooey!* she thought to herself.

Those smug, stuck-up girls who looked down their noses at mere pedestrians as they rode by. And fresh air – what a joke! As far as Charly was concerned, horse stables were pretty stinky places. But more than anything else – and she was not about to admit this to anyone – Charly was irrationally afraid of horses. Just the thought of sitting on the back of one of those gigantic animals was enough to make Charly break out into a cold sweat. Up until now she had successfully refused, but this time the situation looked serious.

Would she really have to go through with this just so that her mother, who worked for a big marketing company, could go to London for a week? Fat chance!

Charly jumped up, took her cell phone from her night table and dialed a number. It rang a few times and just as Charly was about to hang up, someone answered the phone.

"Schultz residence."

A female voice. Charly swallowed.

"I would like to speak with Mr. Schultz, please," she said hoarsely.

Could this be her father's new housekeeper?

"Darling!" called the voice on the other end of the line. "Come over here. Someone wants to talk to you."

"Hello, this is Mr. Schultz. Who's calling?"

Stunned, Charly hung up. What would she have said to her father? That she would like to spend the week that her mother was in London with him? That she missed him?

It didn't matter what she wanted to say to him. It didn't have any meaning anymore. Her father had a new girlfriend. And that meant that Charly had lost him forever. Never in her life had she felt as alone and lonely as she did at that moment.

Chapter 3

"June! What's keeping you?" Marty's voice reverberated through the entire house.

June threw back the blanket and rubbed her eyes. In this house you couldn't even sleep in on a weekend! She slipped on a pair of old jeans, pulled a t-shirt over her head and walked down the stairs.

"Why were you shouting like that?"

"Well, do you think we've got all the time in the world?" Marty slammed a bowl of cornflakes down on the table in front of June. "The Haflingers are waiting for you."

"Oh no, the Haflinger Gang." June sighed and leaned back in her chair. "You just can't get a break around here."

The five Haflinger geldings had proven to be difficult work indeed, which was why Ben nicknamed them the "Haflinger Gang." June couldn't keep track anymore of how many times the five of them had taken the paddock fence apart since their arrival at Sunshine Farm. Once, they were all in the neighbor's cornfield. He was extremely upset and threatened Marty with calling the police. All in all, discipline was not easy with these geldings. When Charly was leading them, they jerked around mercilessly. And when it came to riding, they were able to get their way surprisingly often.

"It's a good thing that at least Lena and Maxi come by to help," said June as she poured herself a glass of orange juice.

"That's for sure," said Marty. "We can use all the help we can get. Just for that, I'm going to invite you all out for pizza at lunchtime."

June smiled. "I know they'll like that."

For awhile, she spooned her cornflakes in silence. Then she looked at her mother.

"Hey, Mom, who's going to be doing the cooking, anyway?"

"What do you mean, cooking?" Marty gaped at her daughter with her eyes wide open.

"You know, cooking. I mean, the campers are going to need something to eat."

"Oh yeah." Marty smiled. "I'll take care of that, of course."

"*You*?"

"What's that supposed to mean?" Marty felt insulted.

"Well, I mean, cooking is, well, uh, you know, um…" June stammered. "I mean, um, you can't really take everyone out for pizza every day. That'd get pretty expensive after awhile, er…"

"Of course I would cook every day," Marty answered, still feeling insulted. "Or are you trying to tell me that I'm not capable of doing that?"

"I, er, well…" June didn't know how to say this. Her mother was pretty much a hopeless case in the kitchen, but June decided to keep that to herself for now.

Fortunately, just at that moment, they heard a loud honking in the courtyard. June jumped up from her chair and ran to the window. A slim blonde woman got out of a small, bright red car.

"Bea's here," June called out, relieved.

Bea was Marty's best friend. The two of them had known each other since elementary school and shared a great love of horses. But Bea only rode when she had a little free time, because her real job was running an accounting office nearby in Forestville. That's why she had said it was okay for Princess, her Trakehner mare, to be ridden during lessons until Marty managed to buy a few other training horses.

June and her mother went downstairs.

"Didn't you want to go for a ride today?" June asked, surprised to see Bea dressed in old jeans and sneakers instead of her riding pants.

"I wanted to, but your mother has a different assignment for me," Bea sighed. "I have to do some painting."

June smiled. Somehow her mother always managed to get others to pitch in and help. So now poor Bea had to paint the rooms in the old dairy kitchen. That's what they called the building directly next to their house. The old dairy kitchen had been empty for years and was now being converted into guest rooms.

Bea got a big pail of white paint and a paintbrush out of the trunk of her little car.

"I guess I'd better get started."

"Wouldn't you like to have a cup of coffee first?" asked Marty.

"Maybe later. I'm planning to go to the theater tonight. I'd like to have all this wrapped up by then."

21

Bea grabbed the pail and brush and strolled over to the old dairy kitchen.

"Isn't it a little cool in there?" June asked Marty as Bea disappeared behind the heavy green door. Yesterday when she, Ben, Maxi and Lena had been cleaning up in there, she was freezing cold.

"Nonsense. You'll see, pretty soon it'll be so hot outside that the kids will be happy to have a room where it's a little cooler." Marty beamed at her confidently. "And now, let's get to work. The Haflingers are waiting."

"Good grief. Who knows what mischief they'll cook up today." June grabbed her chaps from where she had left them next to the front door and slowly headed for the paddock next to the riding ring where Nino, Nano, Navajo, Ninja and Noel were situated. Just as she was about to open the gate, a green station wagon drove up.

"Hey, June!" Lena called from the half-opened window. "Do you want to ride rodeo style again?"

June laughed and shook her head.

Lena and her sister, Maxi, who was younger by a year, shared a Norwegian Fjord horse named Olaf who was boarded at Sunshine Farm. June always found it surprising that they managed to share a horse without constantly fighting about it. Just the thought of someone else sitting on Nelson made her hair stand on end!

As soon as the car stopped, Lena, Maxi and their mother hopped out.

"Hi June," said Mrs. Morris. "Is your mother around?"

"I have no idea." June looked around. "She might be in the dairy kitchen, giving Bea a hand with painting. Want me to go take a look?"

"I'll do it myself." Mrs. Morris bent over to get a

folder out of the side pocket in the door. "She called me yesterday to ask me to bring over a few recipes – ones that are as simple as possible."

"Does your mother really want to cook?" Maxi asked breathlessly as Mrs. Morris disappeared in the direction of the dairy kitchen.

"Sure looks that way," June answered and shrugged here shoulders. "It looks like she's pretty serious about it – although it's a shame that she isn't as talented as your mother."

"Oh, it's no big deal. And anyway, your mother's a great rider," Lena said appreciatively and patted June on the back. "That's a lot more exciting. Hey, let's head over to the Haflinger Gang. Who knows what those fellows will do today."

"I said the same thing a few minutes ago," sighed June, and she walked to the paddock with Lena and Maxi. The chestnuts with the blonde manes and tails were standing peacefully under a big chestnut tree, grazing. When they heard the girls approach, they raised their heads and looked at them inquisitively.

"Don't you think Nino has a totally cute face?" Lena went over to one of the Haflingers and brushed a thick blonde lock off his forehead, revealing a narrow blaze that ran down over his nose.

"Yeah, but I think Noel's cuter," said her sister. "He has such beautiful big eyes and such a pretty white spot on his forehead."

"Hey, hey, don't you go getting jealous now, Nino," laughed Lena. "You're cute, too."

"No surprise," snorted Maxi, laughing. "Considering how little he is."

And in fact the dark chestnut with the broad blaze and pink nose was considerably smaller than his cronies, which all stood at least four inches taller than Nano.

"That's how he got his name," June said and she patted the little Haflinger on his powerful back. "In Italian, Nano means dwarf."

"No worries, Ninja, we haven't forgotten you," said Maxi as a big strong Haflinger simply nudged Nano aside to get closer to the girls. "You know, you're a real bully, Ninja."

"That's for sure," June agreed. "Ninja will steamroll over anything that happens to be in his way. And Navajo is the naughtiest of them all. There hasn't been a single day where he hasn't done something foolish."

"Speaking of which," Maxi let her gaze sweep across the paddock, "Where is Navajo anyway?"

"No idea." June turned around. "But he should be here, shouldn't he?"

"Unless of course…" said Lena.

"…he broke out," Maxi finished her sentence and pointed to a chestnut-colored spot in the bright yellow canola field that adjoined the paddock.

"Oh no!" June called and ran off. "Mr. Myers is gonna flip out if he finds one of our horses in his field again." Mr. Myers was the farmer who owned the field.

Maxi and Lena chased after her. The three of them slipped through the fence and walked along the edge of the field until they were about level with the light colored chestnut with the zigzag blaze. He took one look at the approaching girls, turned and galloped off through the field.

"Oh no!" gasped Maxi. "No, he's trampling everything! Where's he going next?"

"I think he's running toward our farmyard," called June. "Let's run after him! We need to catch him before he ruins everything!"

The three girls ran down the dirt path as quickly as they could in the direction of the farmyard. Once there, they could see Navajo trotting on the pebbles with his head held high. Marty was already at the chestnut's heels, but she didn't stand a chance to catch him. Every time she got close enough, he swerved and ran in the other direction.

"Come on! We'll surround him!" called June. The three streamed off in different directions and closed in on the Haflinger from all sides. He stopped and looked at them, an amused expression under the thick curl on his forehead. Just as June reached for his halter, he shook his head, turned again and galloped off, full speed ahead between June and Maxi toward the dairy kitchen. As she caught her breath, June saw Bea walking out of the door with a bucket of paint in her hand. With eyes wide-open, she stared at the Haflinger that was racing toward her at full speed.

Just as June thought that it was too late, Navajo made a sharp turn to the right and brushed against the bucket in Bea's hand. Bea was so startled that she let go and the bucket hit the ground with a loud crash – its contents splashing out in all directions in a thick shower.

"Oh no!" June couldn't help but exclaim. "Just look at this mess!"

Bea stood there, covered from head to toe in white paint. Stunned, she looked down at her clothes.

"Oh for crying out loud!" she called. "This stuff is everywhere. How am I supposed to get it all off by tonight? And I really wanted to go to the theater!"

She sat down on the stairs leading in to the dairy kitchen and shook her head.

"Oh come on," said Marty who walked over to her right away. "We'll get it off. I'll help you."

June didn't know if she should laugh or cry. Instead she decided to go after the perpetrator. He was now peacefully standing next to the paddock gate, looking over at them. As June approached him, he let her catch him. June fastened the rope to his halter and went over to Marty and Bea.

"You know, Mom, I don't think this is working. You really need to rethink this whole idea about running a riding camp."

Marty turned to her and dug a crumpled piece of paper out of her pants pocket.

"Too late," she smiled. "We got our very first registration today by e-mail. Look – I already printed it out."

"Our first registration?" June grabbed the slip of paper out of her mother's hand and read it.

"Charlotte Schultz, 13 years old, from Washington, DC, no riding experience."

She gave the piece of paper back to her mother.

"Charlotte Schultz," she repeated with a smile. "That poor thing has no idea what she's gotten herself into."

Chapter 4

"Let's go!"

Nelson took the blue-and-white oxer and landed, soft as butter, on the other side of the obstacle.

"Good work, boy."

June slowed the white horse to a walk and let him walk round on long reins. Nelson was truly in top form, despite the fact that she hadn't been able to train with him much during the past few weeks. Training the Haflinger Gang simply took up all of her time.

"And tomorrow the first guests are arriving, Nelson." She ran her fingers through Nelson's gray-black mane. "Can this possibly turn out well?"

June was still concerned about her mother's plans. True, the dairy kitchen was all cleaned up, and with a fresh coat of paint it didn't look half bad, but it was still a long way from an "idyllic atmosphere." Rustic was more like it. It would all be more palatable if only the five Haflingers would learn to behave, at least a little, but the geldings had nothing but nonsense in their heads. Just yesterday Navajo trotted out of the riding ring with June because he was

28

bored with constantly trotting in a circle. June could pull and scold all she wanted – but she was powerless against his mule-headedness. Her mother had to run after them and drag them back to the ring by the reins. June wished she were invisible – it was so embarrassing!

Then Nano recently bucked Maxi off when they were trail riding because a runaway sheep startled him.

"Stubborn and jumpy," mumbled June and took up the reins again. "What a horrible combination."

June praised her Anglo-Arabian, who truly feared nothing and no one. She galloped on and jumped two more times, once from the left and once from the right over the oxer. That had to do for today.

Nelson snorted with satisfaction as she guided him from the ring in the direction of the fields in order to ride another round on the open ground. June joyously patted his neck.

"You were really terrific, boy. If you keep this up, we may even place in the tournament."

The daydreams come to an abrupt halt, however, when June returned to the farmyard with Nelson.

"There you are, at long last!"

Marty seemed agitated as she strode over to her daughter.

"Finish up quickly with Nelson and then come help me set things up in the dairy kitchen."

June looked over at the furniture store truck parked in front of the house.

"Did the beds arrive?"

Marty nodded.

"Five bunk beds for ten children," she said proudly. "I think this is all going like clockwork."

June jumped down from the saddle and glanced

suspiciously at the paddock where the Haflinger Gang was standing. Navajo was standing with his haunches to the gate, pressing so hard against it with his croup that the fence posts cracked. Could that strong blonde be planning another escape? June shook her head. You could never be sure with those Haflingers!

She led Nelson across the courtyard to his hitching post and unsaddled him. Then she put the saddle equipment in the saddle room and groomed his cottony soft, white coat until it glistened in the sun. She took a step back to admire her handiwork. The white gelding turned his elegant head and looked at her with his big dark eyes.

"If this jumping career doesn't work out, you could always perform in the circus as a unicorn," June smiled and stroked his fine mane. Nelson snorted happily and nudged her.

June laughed.

"Of course you get a treat."

She dug in her pants pocket and pulled out a piece of carrot that she held out to him on her flat hand. Nelson carefully took it in his soft mouth and chewed with satisfaction.

"But now we have to get going," said June when he finished. "I'm sure Modena is already waiting for you."

June was right. The black mare trotted over to the fence, her head held high, and whinnied noisily. To June, it almost sounded like an accusation. She opened the gate, unfastened the rope and gave Nelson one last clap on his backside.

"There you go." June hung the rope on the gatepost and headed off toward the dairy kitchen. The men carried one large carton after another into the small building, while Marty ran between them telling them where to set everything down. June stood next to the furniture truck.

"Hi there, everyone," a voice announced.

June turned around and noticed a gray-haired man in riding clothes.

"Hello Mr. Kessler. How, er, are you doing?"

June always felt a little uneasy around this man who had boarded his warmblood, Magister, at Sunshine Farm at the beginning of the month. He was friendly but distant, and June never knew what to say to him.

"Fine, thank you," said Mr. Kessler who then went to the saddle room.

June watched him pensively. She was itching to know what Mr. Kessler did for a living. Ben was convinced that the mysterious man with the silver gray hair had to be the head of an illegal secret organization. Could he be right?

Before June could consider the possibilities any further, Marty returned.

"Let's get going, June. The guys are finished and I need you to help me put everything together."

"Put everything together?"

June stared at her mother.

"Do you mean to say that the beds aren't assembled?"

"Of course not," said Marty and rolled her eyes in annoyance. "Did you think they'd fit into those flat things over there?"

She pointed to the cartons that were stacked up at the entrance to the dairy kitchen.

"Can't the men do that?"

June motioned with her head to the furniture deliverymen who were about to get back into their truck.

"I asked them the same thing," groaned Marty, "but they said that's not their job."

She self-consciously scratched the back of her head.

"To be honest, I thought they'd be delivered fully assembled."

"Now what?"

June went over to the cartons and carefully touched them with the tip of her foot.

"We put them together," said Marty and brushed an unruly strand of red hair out of her face. "The instructions must be in here somewhere."

She tore open one of the cartons with all her strength and pulled out several sheets of paper.

"See? What did I tell you? Here it is."

She sat down on the steps that led into the building and began to read. June simply stood there and waited.

And waited.

And waited.

"Well?" she finally asked, feeling totally impatient. "Do you know what to do now?"

Marty lifted her head and grinned pitifully.

"Here, maybe you can understand what they're talking about."

She passed her the stack of paper.

June skimmed the pages and shook her head.

Lots of lines and arrows pointing in every possible direction.

"I don't understand a single thing."

She sighed and sat down next to her mother.

"Now what?"

Marty shrugged her shoulders.

"I have no idea."

The two sat there in complete silence for awhile and stared into space. Suddenly June jumped up.

"I know! We'll call Ben. I don't know why I didn't think of this sooner!"

Ben just happened to be as handy as they come. Hopefully he was home just then. June ran into the house to the little telephone table in the hallway and dialed Ben's number.

"Hey June, I'm glad you called. I was planning to go down to the stable to ask you if you'd go for a ride with me."

"Nope, I can't ride now," said June quickly. Then she explained her problem.

"Okay, then I guess good old Björn has the day off," said Ben. "My mother will drive me right on over. I'll be there in a half hour."

Relieved, June hung up. At least that was taken care of. The good feeling didn't last long, however. Just as June was about to walk out of the house, the phone rang. June picked up the receiver.

"This is Mr. Myers calling," a deep voice barked into the receiver. "Your darned nags are in my cornfield again. If those rotten creatures aren't off my land immediately, I'll call the police!" Slam!

June stared at the receiver and listened to the buzz of a dial tone. He had hung up!

Like the wind, she dashed out of the house to her mother.

"The Haflingers broke out!" she shouted to her.

Marty looked at her with astonishment.

"What are you talking about? I just checked on them. Take a look yourself. Navajo's standing right over there."

June looked over at the paddock where Navajo was dozing happily under an apple tree. Marty was right –

Navajo really was there. And since he was the undisputed leader of the Haflinger Gang, that meant that the others were probably nearby. June looked around. Could Mr. Myers be mistaken about the horses in his cornfield? But then she spied a hole in the fence.

"Navajo is here!" she called. "But the others aren't."

She walked past the Haflinger gelding who gave her a mischievous look through his forelock. June hesitated a minute. It was as if the strong chestnut was playing lookout for his buddies so that they could sneak out without anyone noticing. But then she shook her head and kept walking. Impossible. No horse would ever think of something like that.

She sighed as she walked to the gatepost where the lead ropes of the runaways hung. Just as she was about to head out, she heard a car driving into the courtyard. It parked in front of their house and Maxi and Lena hopped out.

"Hey June, where are you going?"

"Where do you think? I have to go catch our Haflingers again. They're in Farmer Myers' field. Care to give me a hand?"

"Sure," the sisters call out to her in unison and ran to join her.

"Have fun, girls," Mrs. Morris called after them as she lifted two huge shopping bags out of the trunk. June remembered that Lena and Maxi's mother offered to buy groceries for the first weekend with the campers. Mrs. Morris was really nice to support Marty that way. Still, June kept having a bad feeling that her mother may have taken on too much with this idea, making her too dependent on other people helping her out. But that wasn't her problem right now. She had to focus on catching the runaway Haflingers and calming down Mr. Myers. Because it wouldn't be much longer before their neighbor really did decide to call the police. And even without that, June felt as if she already had enough stuff to worry about...

Chapter 5

"Isn't it beautiful here?"

Vanessa Schultz navigated past the bright yellow canola fields and glanced briefly at her daughter. Charly cowered pitifully in the passenger seat and turned her head in the other direction. She didn't want her mother to see that she had tears in her eyes.

"Mmm hmm," she managed to squeak out, and bit her lower lip to keep from bursting into tears. Her mother had no idea how miserable she felt.

Riding camp! How disgusting!

Just thinking about the possibility that she may just have to sit on top of a horse's back this afternoon was enough to make her feel so utterly panicked that the hair on the back of her neck was standing on end. Why couldn't she just tell her mother that she was petrified of horses and felt extremely uneasy around them? After all, there was no rule that everyone in the world had to love riding horses.

Hopefully she'd at least have her own room so she could cry herself to sleep like she did at home.

"Look over there on the right," said her mother. "Back there, you see, there's someone riding. Doesn't that look great?"

Charly looked out of the window and could see a figure riding a white horse on the horizon. The figure was leaning close to the neck of the horse which, it seemed to Charly, was racing along the edge of the field at a breakneck speed. Was it running away?

"Once you learn to ride, then you can gallop through the fields like that, too. Wouldn't that be fun?"

"Real fun," Charly said ironically and rolled her eyes.

To be honest, she couldn't imagine anything worse than racing across a field on a runaway horse. Well, almost nothing worse.

The worst thing that she could imagine had already happened to her: her parents had separated and her father had a new girlfriend. She had been secretly wishing that her parents would have a romantic reconciliation. Along the lines of: we made a mistake and from now on we'll live happily ever after together. But after that phone call to her father, Charly realized that it was just a silly dream.

Vanessa Schultz stepped on the brake and turned right onto a narrow dirt road through the woods.

"It can't be far now."

"Too bad," Charly mumbled and tried to put up a brave front so that no one noticed how rotten she really felt inside.

Shortly after they emerged from the woods, they reached a hill that led to a large white building.

"There it is," said Vanessa and shifted into a lower gear to make it easier to drive up the hill.

Charly cowered in her seat again and with a gloomy

expression watched the building get closer and closer.

As Vanessa pulled up into the courtyard, she saw that the building was just one part of the farm. Sunshine Farm was built in the shape of a horseshoe, with buildings on three sides and one open side that led to the sprawling paddock.

They got out and looked around. A small woman with fiery red hair approached them. Charly thought that she looked pretty messy in her dirty old riding pants and torn checkered shirt.

"Sunshyne," said the woman and extended her hand.

Charly looked at her suspiciously. What kind of an odd greeting was that?

Vanessa Schultz shook the woman's hand.

"Hello, Mrs. Sunshyne. I'm Vanessa Schultz." She stepped aside to introduce Charly. "And this is my daughter Charlotte. She goes by Charly."

"Hi, Charly. I'm Marty Sunshyne. You can just call me Marty."

Slowly Charly realized that this woman's last name was Sunshyne. What a ridiculous name. She nodded curtly and stuck her hands in her pockets.

Vanessa Schultz looked around.

"I guess we're the first to arrive?"

Marty Sunshyne nodded.

"The other children will be arriving later this afternoon."

"I hope I'm not causing you any trouble, but I had to bring Charly early because otherwise I'd miss my flight."

Marty smiled.

"No problem. I think we'll be able to keep Charly busy until the others arrive. Don't you think, Charly?"

Charly looked at her from beneath her dark bangs and frowned.

"I can keep busy by myself, thank you very much."

"Oh, er, well then..."

Marty looked nervously at Vanessa, who shot Charly a dirty look and went to unload the heavy blue suitcase from the trunk of her BMW convertible.

"You'll have to excuse her. My husband and I just recently separated and it has been hard on Charly."

Charly couldn't believe her ears. Must her mother tell this strange woman everything? The whole world didn't have to know that she was now a child from a broken home!

Marty nodded sympathetically and pointed to a small building next to the large house.

"I'll show you to the room that the girls will be bunking in."

The ROOM? That couldn't possibly mean that she had to sleep in a room with all the other girls, could it? The thought of it made Charly sick to her stomach. But it got even worse.

Not only was there just one room for all the girls, but on top of all that it was pretty ugly too, at least in Charly's opinion. The small windows allowed very little light in. On top of that, it smelled like fresh paint.

"Next door is another small room in which the boys will be sleeping. We have eight girls and two boys," Marty happily chattered on. "More girls seem to be into riding than boys. I have no idea why."

She turned to Charly.

"How long have you been riding, Charly?"

"I don't ride at all," Charly mumbled and sat down on one of the freshly made beds. "I can't stand horseback riding."

Marty's chin dropped. With her mouth wide open she stood there, staring at Charly.

"Charly is still a beginner," Vanessa Schultz quickly

explained. "She's a little shy around horses, but I'm absolutely certain that she'll be an enthusiastic rider by the end of this week."

"Whatever you say, Mom."

Marty gave her a tortured smile and nervously rubbed her hands together.

"Okay then, maybe you'd like to unpack all your things, Charly. I can show you around the farm later."

She rushed so hastily out of the building that she nearly tripped down the stairs on the way out.

"I'll be there in a moment to talk to you," Vanessa Schultz called after her. "I'd just like to say goodbye to my daughter first."

She sat down on the bed next to Charly and put her arm around her shoulders.

"Please Charly, just try to make the best of the experience. You have my phone number in London. I have to go now or I'll really miss my flight. Call me if you need to talk. And we'll see each other again in a week."

She hugged her daughter, gave her a big kiss on the cheek and got up.

"See you later, Charly."

"See you later," Charly repeated quietly and without looking up. Once her mother left the room, she jumped up and looked out of one of the little windows. She watched Vanessa Schultz talking to the odd Mrs. Sunshyne, and then waving to her before getting into her car. As the convertible drove away from the farm, Charly felt like she could burst into tears.

A whole week on this horrible farm in this horrible room and with the horrible woman as her watchdog. How could her mother do this to her?

Just as she went to sit down again, she heard a noise in the courtyard. Hooves? She looked out of the window again. A white horse walked right past her window. There was a girl with him whose blonde hair cascaded out from under her riding helmet. Charly squinted. Could this girl have been the one she saw galloping through the fields earlier? It certainly could've been the horse she saw before. But didn't Mrs. Sunshyne say that aside from her, there weren't any other guests here yet?

Charly looked around the room. Aside from her suitcase, there was no other luggage to be seen. Could it be this girl lived here all the time? The poor thing. Charly shuddered at the mere thought of it. She threw herself on the bed, rolled over on her side and stared at the wall. This was going to be the longest week of her life.

Chapter 6

"Have any guests arrived yet?"

June stormed into the kitchen excitedly. Marty was sitting at the table, slurping her cup of tea and lost in thought.

"While I was out riding, I thought I saw a car come over the hill."

"One guest did arrive," Marty said. She rolled her eyes. "And what a guest it is."

"What do you mean by that?"

June looked at her mother incredulously, who briefly described her first meeting with Charlotte Schultz.

"Maybe you could go over and check on her," Marty suggested. "Maybe she gets along better with people her own age."

June didn't know what to make of this. On the one hand, she had no desire to deal with a cranky city girl, but on the other hand, she was pretty curious about their first guest.

"Alright," she said finally. "I'll go down to her. Maybe she's not so bad after all."

She hopped down the stairs of their house and pulled on her stable shoes outside. Then she crossed the courtyard to the dairy kitchen. The door was open just a crack.

"Helloooo, anybody here?"

She went up the stairs and entered the semi-darkened room. If this camp idea got off the ground, then her mother would have to do something about the windows. They let in too little light, in June's opinion. She let her gaze wander from bed to bed and then saw someone lying in the lower bunk, with her back against the wall. A girl.

"Hello? Are you Charly? I'm June. June Sunshyne. I'm here to welcome you to Sunshine Farm."

The girl just looked at her. June found the silence embarrassing, so she quickly started to chatter.

"I'd like to show you around the farm, and then we can pick out a horse for you to take care of. Would you like to come along?"

The girl slowly got into a sitting position on the edge of the bed. June saw that she had short black hair and was dressed entirely in black. It was a little too grim for June's taste, especially at this time of year.

"Okay," the girl finally said. "We might as well get it over with."

She got up and went out.

June pensively followed her.

What did she mean by, "get it over with"? Her mother was right – Charly really did seem to be a special case. *Are all the camp kids going to be like this,* she wondered as she guided the new guest to the open stable.

"This is Nelson, and this is Modena. Nelson is my horse. He's an Anglo-Arabian," June explained with

44

pride. "Modena belongs to my mother. Modena is an Oldenburger and my mother used to…"

"Can we keep going?" Charly interrupted her abruptly, without taking a closer look at either horse.

"If that's what you want," said June, insulted. She took her to the paddock where Olaf, Björn, Princess and Magister were kept.

"These are our boarding horses. They stay here all year. The little chestnut mare over there is Princess – she belongs to a friend of my mother's. The big brown one is Magister. And the dappled gray horse with the wild mane is…"

"Is there something else I have to look at?" Charly interrupted again.

June swallowed her anger with great difficulty. She could have spared herself the effort. It seemed pretty obvious to June that Charly wasn't the slightest bit interested in horses. Why was she at a horseback riding camp, then? June was baffled and just shook her head. She went over to the Haflinger paddock. With a trained eye she quickly counted if all of the horses were there. One. Two. Three. Four. She held her hand against her forehead so that she could see better in the sun. Ah, yes. Way in the back was little Nano. Five.

"This is the Haflinger Gang," June sighed. "Our, er, school horses. They're from a kind of rescue program."

"Rescue program?"

June couldn't believe her ears. Could Charly actually be showing interest?

"Exactly. They come from an organization that rescues Haflingers from the slaughterhouse."

"The slaughterhouse? Why are they sent there?"

June shrugged her shoulders.

45

"I don't know. I guess because there's no other use for them."

Charly stared at Navajo and Nino with big round eyes. The horses walked over to the fence, looking curious, probably hoping for a treat from this new person. June noticed that her camp guest fearfully backed away when the Haflingers stretched out their big heads toward her.

She's can't really be afraid of horses, June thought. *Here at a riding farm!* But then again, that would certainly be typical of Marty's kind of luck – to have the first guest at her riding camp be afraid of horses. If it weren't so sad, June would have laughed out loud right then.

"And the one back there?"

Charly positioned herself far enough away from the fence and pointed to Nano, who was still standing apart from the others.

"Oh, that's Nano. He's a little shy and likes to stay in the background. Maybe because he's smaller than the others and knows that he's low in the pecking order."

"Ah."

June figured that Charly had had enough and wanted to go back to her room, but the girl stayed rooted to the spot, staring at Nano. June shuffled her feet, unsure of what to do next. She was relieved when she suddenly heard a car drive up to the farm and turn round.

"Oh, that must be the next camp guest. Please excuse me."

She took big strides over to the bright yellow van that had just pulled up to the house. First a woman and three girls and then a boy got out. June approached the woman and stretched out her hand.

"Hello, I'm June Sunshyne."

The woman gave her a friendly smile and shook her hand.

"I'm Angie Hughes. And this is Ronnie, Lila, Carla and Connor."

She motioned to the kids who were standing next to each other like organ pipes, smiling happily.

June thought that they all looked very nice. She had started to worry that all of their guests would be as difficult as Charly!

Before they could say anything else, Marty came out of the house and hurried over to the woman.

"Mrs. Hughes? I'm Marty Sunshyne."

She turned around to June.

"June, please show our guests to their rooms. Mrs. Hughes and I will be right there."

"Okay."

She led Ronnie, Lila, Carla and Connor to the dairy kitchen and said a fervent little prayer that no one complained about it being so dark. But she needn't have worried.

"Hey, cool, bunk beds. I sleep on top," Ronnie called out and climbed into one of the beds.

"I'll take the lower bunk," said Carla. "Then it's not so far if I have to go to the bathroom in the middle of the night."

Lila stood in the middle of the room, looking a little uncertain.

"Are all the other beds still free?"

"All but one," answered June.

She pointed to Charly's bed, which had a large suitcase on it.

"Who's sleeping there?"

"A, er, another camper," June stammered. What else should she say? Fortunately Connor interrupted to ask

47

where the room for the boys was and June didn't have to explain further.

She led Connor to the smaller room next door.

"Just one bunk bed?" the boy with the red hair and freckles asked.

June nodded.

"Only two boys registered."

"Typical," Connor sighed. "Boys are always in the minority when it comes to riding. Who's my roommate?"

"I have no idea. He isn't here yet – hey, maybe that's him arriving now." Just at that moment, another car pulled up outside.

A white station wagon was in the middle of the courtyard. June went out and waited impatiently for the car doors to open.

Finally an older man and two girls got out. June went over to them.

"Hello, I'm June Sunshyne."

"Hello," said the man. "I'm Steve Dodinger. And these are my two granddaughters, Hannah and Jana."

June looked at the two girls. She squinted in surprise. The two looked exactly alike.

"No, no, it's not an optical illusion," laughed Mr. Dodinger. "They're identical twins, which is why you can barely tell them apart."

The two blonde girls laughed and waved a hello to June.

"You have a funny name," said Jana. Or was it Hannah? "June Sunshyne. Who thought that one up?"

"My mother," groaned June. "She has a very special sense of humor."

"Well I think her name is great," said Hannah. Or was it Jana? "That's why we noticed the advertisement.

Sunshine Farm sounds so nice." She turned around. "You live here, right?"

June nodded.

"Wow. I wish I could live on a horse farm. Do you have your own horse?"

"Yes – Nelson. He's over there."

June pointed to Nelson who was standing at the fence curiously watching all the action.

"The white horse over there? Oh he's beautiful! Can I pet him?"

"Sure, but first we need to get your bags…"

Before June could finish her sentence both twins dashed over to the fence and stroked Nelson, who clearly enjoyed the friendly greeting.

Mr. Dodinger sighed.

"Those two girls are worse than a sack of fleas. It'll do their parents a world of good to have a week off from taking care of them."

He bent down and took a bag in each hand.

"Where should I take these?"

June led him to the dairy kitchen where Ronnie, Carla and Lila were in the process of unpacking their things.

"You can just put them next to that empty bed," said June.

She heard another car drive onto the farm. *This is a regular circus*, June said to herself as she zipped outside again. This time an old VW bug drove up. With its brakes squealing, it pulled up next to Mr. Dodinger's station wagon.

Before the car even came to a complete stop, the door on the passenger side whipped open and a boy jumped out. He was tall and slim and his hair was almost pitch black.

49

"Hi, are we at the right place? Is this Sunshine Farm?"

June nodded and looked at him through her wild hair. Why was her mouth suddenly so dry?

"I'm Mark."

"I'm, er, I'm June. June Sunshyne."

"Hello, June."

Mark turned to the woman who was just getting out of the VW. She was wearing a flowery sundress and her long hair was just as black as Mark's.

"Hey, Ma, this is June. I think she's the daughter of the owner."

Mark smiled at June, who suddenly got all flushed.

"I assume I'm the only boy?"

"Not exactly," rasped June. "There's, er, another one."

"Really?"

Mark raised his eyebrows.

His mother laughed.

"Well then sonny, it looks like you're not the only sultan in this harem. And here you go – you can carry your *own* suitcase."

She turned to June. "Watch out for this one," she smirked. "Somehow he always manages to get everyone else to do his work for him."

"Oh come on, Ma, don't go blabbing everything." Mark grabbed his suitcase and winked at June. "Where do I need to go?"

June pointed to the dairy kitchen and followed after him. This was quite an amusing group that they'd gotten here. And it certainly promised to be an exciting week.

Chapter 7

June led Mark past the girls' room to Connor, who was in the process of unpacking his bag.

June introduced them to each other.

"Connor, this is Mark. Mark, this is Connor."

"Nice to meet you," said Mark and shook Connor's hand. His gaze wandered around the room.

"A little dark in here, but otherwise not bad. Would you rather sleep on the top or on the bottom?"

Connor shrugged his shoulders.

"I don't really care. If you want, you can sleep on top."

"Okay, now that we've gotten that settled, I'd like to suggest that you unpack your things and then I'll show you around the farm," said June.

"Good idea," said Mark. "I hope we'll be riding today, too. And I'd also like to get to know the horse I'll be taking care of."

"That's something my mother will decide. On the registration forms there was a question about how long you've been riding. Based on that she'll choose a horse for you."

"Well, I'd like that white horse that was just standing at the fence," said Mark.

"The white horse?"

June gave him a shocked look.

"That's not possible. That, er, isn't, er, a school horse. He belongs to me."

Mark whistled appreciatively.

"That's your horse? Not bad. And you definitely don't lend him out?"

He cocked his head to the side and looked at her pleadingly.

June shook her head energetically.

"No. Never. But I know that my mother will pick out terrific horses for each of you to care for."

June hastened out to the courtyard. Outside she stopped and took a deep breath. *I mean really, this Mark sure had nerve,* she thought. Lend out Nelson! June decided that she needed to protect herself from the boy with the dark hair and the winning smile. Something told her that she had to be prepared to expect anything from him.

Once she had more or less collected herself, she headed in the direction of the house. Another car drove up onto the farm. June turned around, surprised. All the guests they expected had already arrived.

"Hey June, how's it going?"

Ben jumped out of the car and walked over to her.

"Are all of the campers here now?"

June nodded.

"So, tell me…what are they like? Are they nice? Can they ride? What kind of horses…"

"Stop!" June interrupted him with a laugh. "I can't answer all of your questions at the same time. So I'll take them one at a time. Some of them seem really nice. Most of them, actually. As for whether or not they can ride, well, I don't really know yet. And there's one girl I swear she's never been on a horse. And which horses they'll get – I don't know that either."

She frowned suddenly.

"And get this. There's a boy who absolutely wants to have Nelson to look after!"

"Really?" Ben gave her a shocked look. "I hope you were able to set him straight."

June shrugged her shoulders.

"I told him that Nelson is my horse and is never lent out. But I'm not totally sure that he accepted my answer. I hope Mom lays down the law for him."

As if she had been waiting for a cue, Marty came out of the house.

"Oh, June. Hi Ben. Nice that you're here."

She looked nervously in the direction of the dairy kitchen.

"How does it look? Should we gather our guests and show them the farm? After that, each of them can groom his or her horse and then they can all go for a ride before dinner."

"Do you already know who's getting which horse?" June asked quickly.

Marty dug a crumpled piece of paper out her washed out jeans and waved it in front of June's nose.

"Okay now, June. Would you please fetch our guests?"

June went back to the dairy kitchen and first told the girls and then the two boys that it was time for a short farm tour. The guests chattered excitedly as they came out to the courtyard and assembled in front of Marty.

53

"Hello, er, I'd like to give you all a very warm welcome to Sunshine Farm and hope that we all have a wonderful vacation week together. First off, I'd like to show you around the farm and then…"

"I have a question about the horse that I get to take care of," Mark interrupted and took a step forward. "What happens if we're not happy with the horse that's assigned to us? Can we trade with each other?"

June cringed. She knew exactly what he was after. Unlike Marty, who was looking at Mark with a blank expression on her face.

"Er, I don't know. To be honest, I never thought about that. I, uh, would suggest that we first take a walk around and you can see which horse I chose for you."

"Hey," Ben whispered to June, "he sure doesn't beat around the bush, does he?"

"Mm hmm."

June pressed her lips together and frowned at Mark. He smiled innocently back at her and then followed Marty with the others to the paddock where Princess, Magister, Björn and Olaf were quartered. From there, they continued on to the Haflinger paddock.

"Who is that over there?"

Ben pointed to a dark-haired girl with black pants and a black t-shirt standing next to the fence watching the chestnuts graze.

"Oh no, I totally forgot about her. That's Charly. You know, the one who probably hasn't ever ridden before."

"I just hope that your mother doesn't decide to give her one of the Haflingers," Ben grinned.

June chuckled quietly. "No, definitely not. The poor thing would have the shock of her life."

"Charly, would you please join us," said Marty after introducing the Haflingers.

Charly made a face and groaned quietly.

"Whatever," she said and then joined the group as it headed over to Nelson and Modena's paddock.

"That white horse is really beautiful," said Mark expertly as he approached the fence. "An Arabian?"

"An Anglo-Arabian," said Marty. "You know a little bit about horses, huh?"

"Of course. I've been riding for ages," said Mark, casually patting Nelson's neck. The white horse shook his head and withdrew a few steps backward.

June grinned. Nelson was very sensitive and couldn't stand it if someone was too forward with him.

"Alright then."

Marty dug another slip of paper out of her jeans.

"Now I'll be telling you who gets which horse. Then we'll do some grooming and you can ride a little. That way I'll get a better idea of your riding abilities."

She unfolded the paper and read out loud.

"Hannah and Jana, on your registration you wrote that you haven't been riding all that long. You'll be on Modena and Princess. You can decide between yourselves who gets which horse. Both are very gentle and reliable."

The twins smiled brightly and started to discuss which of them got to ride which horse. June stared at them, fascinated, and wondered if she'd ever be able to tell them apart.

"Now let's get to those of you who have more riding experience. Carla, you get Nino. Ronnie, you get Noel, Connor you get Ninja, and Mark, you'll be riding Navajo."

"Navajo?" asked Mark incredulously. "Isn't that one of the…"

"...Haflingers," Marty completed his sentence. "Of all our guests, you were the one with the most experience and Navajo, er, well, Navajo is not as far along as the others in his training."

"Not as far along in his training," Ben whispered and playfully pinched June in the side. "That's another way of putting it."

"I'm supposed to ride a Haflinger?"

"Of course. What's wrong with that?" asked Ben.

Marty looked at him, surprised.

"Do you have a problem with Haflingers?"

"Well, yes." Mark brushed a strand of black hair out of his face. "Actually, I thought that I'd be getting something cooler. Like an Arabian, for instance. What's with the white horse over there?"

He pointed to Nelson, who was standing next to Modena and grazing peacefully.

June balled her hands into fists. He knew perfectly well that Nelson belonged to her!

"That's June's horse," said Marty. "He is not available for others to ride. Go ahead and give Navajo a try first. Unless..."

She paused briefly and then smiled at Mark.

"...You're afraid. As I said, he's not easy."

"Afraid? Hah! What nonsense. Of course I'm not afraid. Okay then, I'll try him."

June gave her mother an appreciative look. She hadn't expected Marty to think so well on her feet. Although, on the other hand, it was obvious that you could convince someone like Mark pretty quickly that way.

"Good. Then we have one more horse to give out."

Marty's gaze wandered to Charly, who had been standing by apathetically staring into space.

56

"Charly, on your registration it said that you've never ridden before. For you we have something very special. You'll ride Björn. He is an Icelandic and a very sweet horse."

"That is, unless he falls too far behind when you're riding on the trails," Ben said quietly and giggled.

June looked at him with surprise. Wasn't he mad that Mrs. Hanson had made Björn available for the campers? Obviously not, because Ben went over to Charly and told her in a good-natured way, "Björn is a real gem. You don't have to worry about anything with him. Would you like me to help you get him from the paddock?"

Good old Ben. Always there to lend a hand when somebody needed help.

But Charly apparently didn't want any help.

"No, you don't need to," she whispered. "Because I'm not even going to get him from the paddock."

"What?" Ben couldn't believe his ears.

"I said that I'm not getting that old nag from the paddock." Charly repeated herself so loudly that she caught Marty's attention, who then came over to them.

"What did you just say?"

"I said that I won't bring the nag in from the paddock," Charly said, even louder.

June saw how quickly her mother's face turned red. A clear sign that she was really angry. That's not something that happened often. But when it did, things could get very unpleasant.

"Now you listen to me, dear," said Marty, hands on her hips. "If you don't like it here, then I will gladly call home and ask for someone to pick you up immediately. That's absolutely not a problem. But I don't want to ever, and I'll say it again, ever hear you call any of our horses nags. Have I made myself clear?"

Suddenly everyone went silent and stared at Marty with wide-open eyes. No one had expected the small woman to even be capable of getting so angry. But when it came to horses, Marty was totally serious.

"Have I made myself clear?" she asked again.

Charly opened her mouth to say something, but apparently she couldn't think of any comeback for Marty.

Finally, she nodded.

"Okay, then we've gotten everything cleared up," said Marty in her normal, professional tone of voice.

"Now, please get your horses ready."

Chapter 8

Charly slowly followed her roommates, who were taking the quickest possible route to the dairy kitchen in order to put on their riding clothes. By the time she finally tossed her bag onto the bed, the others were almost ready to go.

Repulsed, Charly pulled out the black boots and the beige riding pants with the leather seat. Her mother had purchased them for her in the hopes that Charly would finally discover a love of riding, which was far from reality. Although Charly dutifully pulled on her boots whenever she had to go to the stable with her mother, she had never sat on a horse in them.

She pulled on her pants – another gift from her mother, bought in one of the most expensive equestrian tack shops in DC – and forced herself into the boots.

How people could willingly put on such uncomfortable things was beyond her! And you couldn't really move very well in them anyway.

Charly gracelessly waded across the courtyard to where the other guests were already busily grooming their horses. Except for the boy with the dark hair, all of

59

them seemed to be in incredibly good moods. With a big frown, he groomed one of the small chestnut horses that she had observed earlier. Somehow Charly felt drawn to the chestnuts. No surprise really, because in a way they shared the same fate. *Welcome to the Club of Unloved*, she thought darkly.

Over there, near the girl with the light brown hair, stood the little chestnut that appeared to be afraid of the others. If she absolutely had to ride, then she would prefer that horse. He looked nice somehow, with his light-colored mane and gigantic, friendly eyes. For a horse, that is.

She definitely didn't want to know what the redheaded woman with the messy hair had in store for her. And the big deal she made just because she said *nag*. Charly rolled her eyes. If only this miserable week would at least go by quickly!

"Ah, there you are, finally."

The boy who had offered to get her pony from the paddock approached her.

"I got Björn already. He's standing over there."

With his head he pointed to a small round white horse whose mane looked as if he'd just received an electrical shock. It stood up in all directions and looked terribly unkempt.

"Björn is a genuine Icelandic," said the boy, sounding quite proud.

"Oh really?" said Charly lamely.

"I'm Ben, by the way, and you're Charly, right?"

The boy smiled from ear to ear. Did he really have no idea how much he was getting on her nerves, she wondered?

She looked at the white horse and swallowed. More

than anything, she wanted to turn on her heels and run back to her room. Away from this nasty animal that had its head turned toward her. The boy took her by the arm and gently but assertively led her to the pony.

Charly felt as if she were being led to her own execution.

"Here."

The boy – Ben – pressed a brush into her hand. She remembered seeing something like it in the stable with her mother. It was a currycomb. At least she thought that's what it was. She barely listened when her mother went on and on about horses.

"Go ahead and start grooming him, and I'll go get the saddle."

Ben walked off and Charly stood there with the currycomb in her hand, staring at the pony. Slowly she placed it on his neck and began currying.

Marty came by.

"You can go ahead and get a little closer. Björn is very gentle. He wouldn't hurt a fly."

Charly gnashed her teeth and moved a little closer to the pony, which was simply standing there quietly, paying no attention to her whatsoever.

As she finished the first side, Ben came back with the saddle.

"Oh no, we have to hurry now," he said, with an eye on the other campers who had already saddled up their horses. "Hold this a second." He thrust the saddle into her hands and quickly curried the pony's other side.

"You won't be winning any beauty contests with this effort, but at least we can saddle him up now."

Ben lay the saddle on, tightened the girth and snaffled Björn.

61

"The riding helmets are in the equipment closet in the stable hall. You can just take one from there. In the meantime, I'll wait here for you with Björn. And hurry up, the others are already riding in the ring."

In fact, the entire group was slowly getting into motion. Charly was in anything but a hurry, so she went into the stable as slowly as possible. She grabbed a riding helmet from the closet and put it on and it seemed to fit okay.

All right then.

She took a deep breath and went back to Ben and the pony.

"I'll help you up and then I'll lead you in to the ring. Marty said that June should start off with lunging you."

Charly moaned to herself. Actually she didn't have any objections to being taken on the lunge. She knew from her mother's stable that a lunge line was sort of a long leash that you use to walk the horse in circles. Which means that at least she wouldn't be subject to the horse's every whim. On the other hand, she didn't like the idea of a girl her age telling her what to do. Especially when it was the daughter of the woman that Charly found so completely annoying.

What do they all call her? Marty. Charly shuddered. What a horrible name.

Once they reached the ring, Charly saw the other campers riding around in step. Marty stood at the fence, in conversation with a woman Charly hadn't seen before.

"Hi Charly. Okay, let's get going."

Charly hadn't even noticed that June had come over to her. She attached the lunge line to the left snaffle ring and encouraged Björn with the lunge whip. Charly cringed. Did June want her to fall off or something?

"Just stay loose, okay?" June smiled. "Old Björn won't run off. A bomb would have to go off next to him before he'd even consider breaking into a gallop when he's on the lunge. And even then I'm not sure he'd do it."

Charly tightly clutched the side rein that was attached to the front of the saddle.

"I'm going to let Björn do a few rounds walking so that you get a feel for him. You need to sit up straight and feel yourself into his movements."

Charly pressed her lips together and clawed her hands even more tightly around the side rein. *Just don't let go*, she thought.

"When you feel confident enough, then you can alternate letting go with one hand."

Charly looked forward with a steely expression and acted as if she hadn't heard what June had just said.

Suddenly she noticed that Björn came to a stop. Relieved, she looked at June.

"Are we done?"

"Done?" June laughed. "We've barely gotten started. I thought we could do a few exercises while standing in place first."

"Exercises?" Charly grunted. "What kind of exercises?"

"Just let go with your left hand and bend your upper body forward until you can touch the front of your left foot."

Charly looked at June as though she had just asked her to jump from the top of the Washington monument.

"Okay people," she heard Marty calling out to the riders on the other side of the ring. "Now take the reins and start trotting. But just a light trot so that the horses loosen up."

"It's not so bad," June said encouragingly. "I promise you that nothing can happen. You just have to…"

She didn't have a chance to finish her sentence because they suddenly heard loud shouting noises coming from the other end of the ring. Charly turned around, frightened, and saw the black-haired boy's chestnut break into a gallop and run for the exit.

"Sit deep in the saddle! Tighten your legs!"

Whatever Marty meant by that, it wasn't any use because in front of the exit, which was locked shut with a wooden plank, the chestnut horse planted all four hooves in the ground and came to a screeching stop. The black haired boy was thrown forward and flew over the horse's neck in a high arc. He landed on the ground with a loud thump.

Charly watched, her mouth hanging wide open. Hadn't she always known that riding was a dangerous sport?

The black haired boy stood up and rubbed his backside in pain. Fortunately, nothing really bad had happened to him.

"Hold on to him!" called Marty. "Just hold on to him!"

The chestnut, which up until then had stood peacefully next to the boy, suddenly jumped to the side, bucked off and galloped toward the other horses at breakneck speed. The two girls riding the black horse and the chestnut were able to guide their horses to safety in the corner. The other children didn't have as much luck. The chestnuts seemed to have been waiting for a sign from their ringleader and now were chasing him all over the ring in a wild gallop as if on command.

"Ben!" June screamed. "Hold on to Björn, I have to help!"

Ben ran over and led the Icelandic into the corner.

"Why aren't we getting out of the ring?" Charly shouted frantically. "Get me out of here immediately!"

"Sorry, that's impossible now," said Ben. "If I push the plank aside, then the other horses will race out of here, one after the other. We'll just stand here until it's over. And don't worry. Björn doesn't do silly stuff like that."

Charly held onto the side rein so tightly that her knuckles turned white. She was totally shocked to see how the girl on the smallest chestnut landed in the sand and how right after that, the other two girls were thrown from their saddles, too. Only the boy held his own, although his horse was still galloping around and around the ring while Marty and June tried to catch the other chestnuts. On top of everything else, one of the horses – Charly thought it was the one that started all the craziness – threw himself onto the sand with his saddle and snaffle still on and started to roll around with pleasure. As he righted himself, his front legs got tangled in the reins, which made him run off and tear the reins with one jerk.

To Charly it seemed to take forever before all the horses were rounded up and the chestnut with the boy finally came to a stop.

"Congratulations, Connor!" June called out, exhausted, as she led two of the chestnuts out of the ring. "You did a super job staying in the saddle."

Marty followed her with two more chestnuts. Her face was bright red.

"Okay, I'd like to suggest that we call it a day. What do you think?"

Charly nodded vigorously.

That was the most sensible thing she'd heard Marty say.

Chapter 9

Two snaffle bits, one stirrup strap, one tendon boot and a saddle blanket."

Marty stood in the saddle closet, shaking her head and tallying up everything that had broken during the campers' first hour of riding.

"I've never experienced anything like that before."

She sighed, sat down on an upside down container and looked at June.

"I mean, I wonder when these Haflingers are finally going to stop all their foolishness."

June would have loved to tell her that she didn't believe that the Haflingers would ever stop their foolishness, but her mother looked so downcast that she decided it was better not to say anything at all. Instead she went over to her and put her arm around her shoulders.

"And then there's that girl with the black hair, Charly," Marty mumbled with a tone of exasperation. "I think she hates me."

"Oh don't be silly. You can't say a thing like that. She was a little nervous, that's all." June explained.

"Do you really think so?" Marty looked at her hopefully. June nodded.

Then Mrs. Morris stuck her head in the door.

"Marty? Dinner's ready. Would you tell the kids?"

Marty got up and clapped the dirt from her pants.

"Thank you, Cheryl. It's so nice of you to help me this first week of camp. I don't know what I'd do without you."

June didn't know either. If it weren't for Mrs. Morris, they'd have had nothing for dinner tonight because Marty hadn't entered the house since the riding lesson. June asked herself how her mother expected to find the time to cook in addition to giving riding lessons, cleaning the stable, leading riding trail rides and everything else that had to be done at a real riding camp. But she couldn't worry about that tonight.

June suddenly noticed that her stomach was growling and it occurred to her that she hadn't eaten in quite some time. What could Mrs. Morris have cooked up tonight?

At any rate, she did a beautiful job setting the big table under the chestnut tree. Lena and Maxi helped her although they were sorry not to have seen Mark fall off Navajo.

"That guy acts likes he's Brad Pitt," Lena whispered to June while Mrs. Morris and Marty carried the food out to the table. "Serves him right that Navajo threw him."

June shrugged her shoulders.

"I don't know. To be honest, I'd prefer that he got along with Navajo. I'm afraid that Mom might just let him ride Nelson if he keeps on bugging her."

"But that would be incredibly mean if she let him do that. After all, she made you a promise!" Maxi was outraged.

68

"That's for sure," June spooned a huge serving of potatoes and stew onto her plate. "But when she made it, she had no idea of what she'd be dealing with. I don't think she had the slightest inkling of what it would mean to run a riding camp. I almost wish she never came up with the idea."

"All beginnings are difficult," Lena consoled her. "You'll see, once we get a routine going, it'll be smooth sailing."

June stuffed a big chunk of stew in her mouth and let her gaze wander around the table. Despite the incident with the Haflingers, all the guests were in a good mood. Well, most of them were.

While all the others stuffed themselves and happily conversed, Mark and Charly sat wordlessly at their places with long faces.

June wondered how Charly ever came up with the idea of going to riding camp, of all things. She had never met anyone who was as afraid of sitting on a horse. Thank goodness Björn hadn't joined in the foolishness of the other horses. Considering the cramped way Charly was sitting on him, she would had fallen off at the first little hop.

Then she remembered what her mother said to her in the saddle room. She couldn't imagine that anyone in the world could hate Marty. Marty was chaotic, impulsive and not exactly diplomatic all the time, but she truly had a heart of gold. It must just be a figment of Marty's imagination.

Right at that moment, Charly's gaze landed on Marty, who had just set a bowl of steaming potatoes on the table. Charly's eyes glimmered angrily and her lips were nothing more than a thin red line on her pale face.

June was shocked. Could her mother be right after all? Whatever the case, there was definitely something strange about Charly.

"How would you like it if tonight we all watch a DVD in our living room?" asked Marty and looked at the group. "I figured that after traveling here and having your, er, first riding lesson, that you might just be a little tired and would enjoy relaxing with a movie."

"All right!" Hannah and Jana call out in perfect unison and the others sounded excited too.

"What kind of a movie are we watching?" asked Mark, who showed interest in something for the first time since his fall. "What kind of movies do you have? I like action movies."

"Um, I don't really have that many movies," said Marty apologetically. June wondered if her mother had any at all, because normally they almost never watched any television. "I especially rented one that I thought you'd all enjoy. What do you think about Hidalgo?"

"Isn't that the movie about the Mustang that wins against an Arabian Thoroughbred?" asked Ronnie. "I've always wanted to see that one."

"Me too!" Björn shouted out. "I read somewhere that the star of that movie also played a role in 'Lord of the Rings'."

A mustang and an Arabian Thoroughbred? June hadn't seen the film either, but thought that it sounded quite exciting.

"If we have to," said Mark in a bored tone of voice. "At least there are Arabian Thoroughbreds in it, because that sure makes a nice contrast to those clumsy Haflingers." He gave June a bold smile. "Arabians just happen to be my favorite kind of horse. Did you know that?"

71

June's face flushed red with anger, and in her pockets she balled her hands into fists. Mark didn't have to act this way. She knew exactly what he was getting at. She stared at him, furious.

"Don't get upset," Ben whispered in her ear. "That's exactly what he wants you to do."

"I know," June sighed, "but every time he starts in with that, it drives me up a wall."

"Speaking of walls," said Lena, who had just joined them. "Come on and let's go into the house or we'll miss the beginning of the movie."

"Huh?"

June looked at her, baffled.

"And what does that have to do with walls?"

"Oh come on, June!" Lena slapped her forehead with the flat of her hand. "Arabian Thoroughbreds. Desert. Fortress. Walls. Get it?"

"That's one strange chain of free associations," grinned June. "How is anyone supposed to follow that?"

"A chain of what?" Now it was Lena's turn to look baffled.

"June is just trying to say that you have a pretty odd way of thinking." Ben translated, although not very true to the original. "Although it's not as if we didn't already know that."

He laughed and moved to avoid being hit by Lena, walking in the direction of the house.

"And now hurry up already or we really will miss the beginning of the movie."

June smiled and followed Lena and Ben with her eyes as they raced wildly toward the house. She decided to stop to see Nelson one more time before joining the others.

As she opened the gate, the white gelding approached her and let out a friendly whinny. June dug around in her pants pocket and pulled out a treat. It looked like it had been through at least one wash cycle already, but that didn't bother Nelson. She offered the treat to the gelding on her flat outstretched hand and tenderly observed how he chewed it with great pleasure. When he finished, she wrapped her arms around his soft neck and breathed in his wonderful sweet scent.

"Oh Nelson," she whispered. "I'll never let that awful person ride you, don't you worry."

She released him and brushed his silky soft forelock out of his face. Nelson looked at her with his big dark eyes, as though he had understood every word.

"Sleep well, sweetie."

June gently blew a kiss to his forehead and this went through the gate. Up at the house she could already see the bluish light of the television through the living room window. She had to hurry or she wouldn't understand what was going on in the movie. But just as she got ready to run, she saw the front door of the house open and a figure emerge. In the twilight, June squinted so that she could recognize who it was from a distance. She held her breath. Charly! Why wasn't she with the others?

June thought about whether she should approach her and ask. She'd probably do that with just about anyone else, after all, and it could be that Charly wasn't feeling well because she was homesick. But something held her back from making her presence known to the dark-haired girl who now looked around, left and right, and then walked to the building in which the saddle room was.

June was torn. Should she follow Charly? She looked

73

upstairs longingly and thought about how comfy the others must be, sitting in front of the television watching a horse movie. Normally June didn't care much for movies, but it was different if there were horses in them. Besides, she was pretty much wiped out after the events of the day and would have liked nothing better than to get comfortable on the shaggy living room carpet.

Indecisively she looked in Charly's direction. She had already disappeared into the building. Shortly thereafter, the light in the saddle room went on.

Should she or shouldn't she?

June took a deep breath and went into the house. Why should she let this strange Charly person ruin her evening, too? There had been enough problems today. Besides, what harm could Charly do in the saddle room? She probably just forgot something in there and was going back to grab it now. June went into the house and closed the door behind her.

Chapter 10

Charly quietly closed the door of the saddle room behind her and walked down the dark hallway of the stable. She slowly felt her way along the cool wall. Outside in the courtyard, she looked around. No one was in sight. They were probably all sitting in front of the television watching that stupid movie. Actually, Charly liked to watch television, but a movie about horses – never! Charly snorted dismissively. That horrible Marty had one idiotic idea after another. She'd see what that would get her.

Charly thought about what to do next. She definitely didn't want to join the others and was happy to have a few minutes of peace alone. That went for the people from the farm as much as for the other kids. The only person she didn't find all that odious was the dark-haired boy that she felt so sorry for when he fell off the horse. Charly could completely understand why he was so mad.

Should she just go back to her room? No. Charly shook her head reluctantly. All she'd do there would be lie on her bed and read or fall asleep. But Charly was too worked up to do either right now. She let out a heavy sigh. Aside from riding, there really was nothing else to do here. And after what had happened this afternoon, Charly felt like she had had more than enough of riding. Horses were just horrible.

Most of them, that is. Charly considered things for a moment. The little chestnut with the light colored mane and tail – he seemed different from the others somehow. Where was his paddock again? She looked around and saw the biggest of the five chestnuts standing in front of the gate. Ah yes, back there! Charly walked over to it. The chestnut standing in front inquisitively pushed his head out as she approached. Charly stopped a few feet away from him. She wasn't exactly sure, but from here it looked like the one that threw the boy.

Charly walked a bit further along the fence and tried to get a better look in the partial darkness at the horses that were standing under the fruit trees, grazing. It was not very easy to tell them all apart. With their chestnut coats and light colored manes and tails they all look pretty similar.

Then one of the horses raised its head and looked out at her from under his light-colored forelock. That was the one! Charly saw now that he was quite a bit smaller than the others. Without even thinking about what she was doing, she walked closer to the fence and stretched out her hand to him. The little chestnut slowly approached and carefully sniffed her. Silly that she didn't bring along an apple or something like that. Charly knew from her mother that horses were always happy when you brought them a treat.

"You poor thing," she said and gently stroked his soft nose. "You're just like me here because no one else wants you."

The little chestnut came nearer, and Charly was able to observe him more closely. He had relatively short, stocky legs and was very muscular despite his smaller stature. Completely different from Dream Girl, her mother's mare. From her mother, Charly knew that Dream Girl was a Hanoverian with a top pedigree. Dream Girl's grandfather was a very famous stallion. What was his name again? Oh yes, Donnerhall. Charly wrinkled her nose. What dumb names these horse people always came up with. In contrast to this little chestnut, Dream Girl had high legs and her long body was gigantic. Her mother said that the mare's height measured 16.3 hands.

Charly thought about her mother and sighed. She'd probably just landed in London and was on her way to the hotel. Why couldn't she have just taken her along? She surely wouldn't have been a burden for her. She couldn't possibly be planning a...?

Charly was nauseated by the thought that her mother might not be in London just for business reasons. Now that her father had a new girlfriend, she wouldn't be surprised if her mother suddenly turned up on the doorstep with a new boyfriend. Charly shook herself. Her mother wouldn't do that to her.

Or would she? She wasn't at all sure what to think.

The little chestnut became bolder and nudged her. Charly, who had completely forgotten where she was, shuddered. The chestnut was startled, took a few steps backwards and came to a stop. He snorted nervously and looked at her from under his thick blonde forelock. Charly stepped closer to the fence.

"Hey, I'm sorry, I'm didn't mean to startle you," she said quietly. "Come back over here."

77

The chestnut looked at her intently, as if he were considering his options. Then he shook his head, spun around and galloped off in the other direction.

Charly pensively watched him go. Why was he so fearful? He must have had some bad experiences with people. Just like Charly. She too had been deeply disappointed during the past few months. And by her own parents, no less!

Charly suddenly felt a deep connection to the chestnut, who was now standing off by himself, away from the other horses, grazing.

Chapter 11

"Hey everyone, have you heard?"

Connor came steaming around the corner like a freight train and skidded to a stop in front of the wooden post where the campers had tied their horses.

"We're going on a trail ride with the horses this afternoon."

"Wow!" Hannah and Jana call out in unison. "That's terrific!"

"A trail ride?" asked June, who had just joined the group with Ben. "Who told you that?"

"Well, your mother did, of course. She said that this morning we should go to the ring one more time and then out on the trails this afternoon."

June gave Ben a horrified look and pulled him aside.

"Has she gone totally crazy?" she whispered nervously in his ear. "She can't possibly take the Haflinger Gang out on the trails after what happened yesterday in the ring!"

"I have no idea, but your mother generally tends to know what she's doing."

Ben scratched the back of his head, lost in thought.

"Er, I mean when it comes to horses. But why don't you ask her yourself? Look behind you, 'cause she's coming this way. In the meantime I'll go help Charly with grooming."

June watched him go, shaking her head. Ben was the only person at Sunshine Farm who didn't let Charly's moods get to him. She approached her mother.

"Hey, Mom, this idea with the trail ride, do you actually mean…"

"Just look at this."

Marty held up the expensive snaffle bit made of English leather that she'd recently purchased for Modena – despite all their financial worries.

June stared at her.

"What?"

"Just look at this," Marty repeated and held the snaffle bit even closer to June's eyes.

Now June saw what her mother was talking about. The leather strap that was fastened to the left side of the bit was ripped. June looked at it again. Ripped wasn't the right word for it. To be more exact, it looked like it had been cut.

"But that looks like…"

"Someone destroyed my expensive snaffle bit on purpose," said Marty, and she angrily stomped the ground with her foot. "What a rotten thing to do."

"Do you really think someone did that on purpose?"

"What else could have happened? The snaffle bit was brand new – it can't possibly rip that easily. Besides, if it did, it would look different. Just wait until I get my hands on the person who did this."

Swinging the snaffle bit she marched off toward the campers who were just in the process of grooming their horses.

"Just a minute please." Marty held the snaffle bit up in the air.

"Did any of you break my snaffle bit yesterday?"

All of them shook their heads and look at her curiously.

"Okay, if it was one of you, then I'd like to ask that person to come to me, by this evening, to confess. Otherwise…"

Her voice grew more serious.

"… Otherwise that person will be thrown out of the camp immediately if I find out who it was some other way. Have I made myself clear?"

Furious, she turned on her heel and marched off angrily. The others murmured nervously amongst themselves and resumed grooming their horses again, one after the other.

June observed the scene from several feet away. She couldn't, by any stretch of the imagination, picture any of their guests doing such a thing. But then her heart began to beat wildly as she suddenly recalled seeing Charly go into the saddle room last night. Her gaze moved to the dark-haired girl standing next to Björn. She was looking at Marty. Was June mistaken, or did she see a smile at the corner of Charly's mouth? June shook her head. No, while Charly wasn't especially likeable, that didn't mean that she would destroy other people's things.

Or would she?

June didn't know what to think anymore. Should she tell her mother that she saw Charly going into the saddle room? Or should she keep it to herself for now and talk to Ben first? Because if she were to go to Marty now, then considering how upset she was, she would probably, in her direct manner, immediately storm over to talk to Charly. And as long as June wasn't completely certain, she'd prefer to avoid that.

"Hey there," Ben said to June as the campers finished saddling up and mounting their horses. "Do you really believe that it was one of them?"

June shrugged her shoulders.

"No idea. But I absolutely have to tell you something."

She quickly reported to him everything that she had observed the night before.

"I don't know," said Ben when she finished. "Why would she have done that?"

"I think she just doesn't like Mom," said June. "And she doesn't like horses. But most of all, she doesn't want to be here. Maybe she's just angry about that and is blaming Mom for everything."

Ben raised his eyebrows.

"That's a little far-fetched, don't you think?"

June sighed.

"Well, I guess. But I know I saw her in the saddle room, at a time when she thought everyone else was in the living room watching a movie. What do you think – should I tell Mom about it or hold off for a while?"

Ben thought it over and then, in his quiet, clear manner, considered a list of her options.

"Can I make a suggestion?" he asked finally.

June nodded.

"Of course."

"What do you think if for now, we don't say anything at all and just observe Charly instead? If we catch her red-handed, then at least we're positive that she's the one who did it. And who knows? Maybe it was someone totally different and we'll find out because we're keeping an eye on everything.

June agreed, relieved. The thought of tattling on Charly to Marty bothered her for several reasons. For one thing, she had no idea what Charly actually did in the saddle room. Maybe she had forgotten something in there. And for another thing, it probably wouldn't be especially helpful for the continued existence of Sunshine Farm for Marty to accuse their first guest of such a serious transgression without any clear evidence. The problem with her mother was that she was just so impulsive.

"June! Ben! What's keeping you?"

Marty was standing on the other side of the farm, waving to them.

"Move it – we'd like to finally get started."

June and Ben quickly went to the ring where the campers had already mounted their horses. Only Charly was standing next to Björn in the middle of the ring, looking at the others. June almost felt sorry for her because she looked so lost. She grabbed the lunge from the bench that stood next to the entrance of the ring and walked over to her.

"Okay, then, let's get started." She said and attached the lunge to Björn's snaffle bit.

Charly looked gloomy but allowed herself to be tossed onto Björn's back without any resistance. The chubby Icelandic with the thick mane stood there placidly and waited until she got into the correct sitting position. June let the lunge out longer and allowed him to walk. Charly sat ramrod straight on his back and looked ahead grimly.

84

Just as June wanted to start the Icelandic on a trot, Ben came over to her.

"Your Mom said I should continue with lunging. She would like to divide the lesson into two groups, with you leading one of them."

June gratefully passed the line to him. Lessons with the Haflinger Gang weren't exactly a piece of cake, but at least it was better than dealing with sourpuss Charly. She walked over to Marty, who was in the process of dividing up the ring with poles.

"It's a little tight, but tomorrow we can teach one group after the other. This will have to do for the first time. I'll take Nino, Ninja, Navajo and Noel in my group. You get Princess, Modena and Nano."

June breathed out a sigh of relief. This was getting better all the time. Princess and Modena were extremely well-trained riding horses that were excellent for giving lessons. And of all the Haflingers, Nano was the most manageable. June often thought that he probably would be relatively easy to handle if only the other Haflingers weren't always getting out of control.

"Okay, then let's get started," she said as Carla and the twins rode over to her circle. "Jana goes in front with Modena, then Hannah with Princess and Carla with Nano at the end. And now, an ordinary trrrrrrrot, light trot."

The hour didn't go badly at all. The three girls could ride very well and since the two mares managed their rounds so skillfully, little Nano rose to the occasion and was suddenly very good as well. June periodically glanced over at the other group, where things weren't quite so peaceful. Mark was constantly struggling with Navajo, and while he didn't bolt today, he apparently wanted nothing more than to stand in place for the entire hour. And when things got too hectic with his impatient rider, he just walked into the middle of the circle and stood there like a statue. June bit her lower lip. Why did Navajo have to turn everything into a circus? If he didn't knock it off soon, Mark would start carrying on again about wanting to ride Nelson!

Nino, Ninja, and Noel weren't in any rush either, and they bumbled lackadaisically around the circle. Marty was quite satisfied with them, as she explained to June after the lesson was over.

"You see, they're already a lot calmer. They just need to work on a more regular schedule, and then the rest will come naturally. Our trail ride this afternoon will do them good."

Oh yes, the trail ride! June had almost completely forgotten about that. "Don't you think it's a little early for that?"

"What do you mean? They were very good today."

June looked doubtfully at her mother. While it was true that the Haflingers were, relatively speaking, very well behaved today, that could just be the proverbial calm before the storm. At any rate, she wasn't convinced when it came to the brawny chestnuts.

"And what will you do with Charly? You can't possibly take her on the trail ride."

"I've come up with an idea for that," Marty said, smiling triumphantly at June. "Lena and Maxi gave their okay for Ben to ride along on Olaf. He can take Björn as a hand pony."

Marty seemed to have thought of everything. But there was one thing June didn't understand.

86

"Which horse are you riding? Someone has to lead the trail ride. Ben will have enough on his hands with Charly and Björn."

"I'll take Magister. Mr. Kessler isn't around this week and he said he'd appreciate it if I give him some exercise. And anyway…"

She smiled at June. "And anyway, you'll be there of course, won't you?"

"Me?" June asked, startled by the question. "I wanted to train with Nelson today, for the tournament."

"Oh come on. Tomorrow's another day for that."

"The tournament is coming up soon," said June. "And anyway, it's bad enough that you don't have any time to train with me and I have to do everything alone."

Marty sighed.

"I know that this riding camp business is pretty exhausting. For me, too, you know. But I promise you that it'll get better once things get rolling. You still have to have a little patience, okay?"

Marty linked arms with June and looked at her imploringly.

"Please, June, just this one time. If you do it then I'll train tomorrow evening with you, okay?"

June sighed. Sometimes she felt as if their roles were reversed – that she was the mother and Marty was the child whom you just couldn't refuse.

"Okay, I'll come along."

Chapter 12

"Yeehaw! We're finally ready to go!"

At almost the exact same moment, Jana and Hannah swung themselves onto Princess and Modena and sat up straight in the saddle. Charly shook her head. How could those two be so happy about this? A trail ride was almost the worst thing that she could imagine. She didn't even want to think about all the things that could go wrong.

But Marty hadn't given her any choice in the matter. Charly was there for riding camp and that meant she had to participate in the program, as she was told after lunch. Otherwise she had to call her father and ask him to pick her up.

Charly snorted contemptuously. That was one thing she was sure of – she never wanted to see her father again. She'd probably have to spend the rest of the week with him and his new girlfriend in the house on the Potomac where she and her mother and father used to be so happy.

All things considered, she preferred going riding. At least the boy would ride along. What was his name again? Oh yes, Ben. Somehow everything here just went whizzing over her head – faces, names, and even entire days.

Charly watched Ben as he pulled the girth tight on Björn and the other horse. He was actually pretty nice. Much nicer anyway that that horrible Marty and her daughter who were always acting like riding was the most fun thing in the world. If they only knew!

"Done." Ben turned his freckled face to her and reached Björn's reins up to her. "Here, you can mount now."

This morning on the lunge, he had shown her how to get on a horse by herself. At first Charly hadn't wanted to, but she'd eventually let him convince her to try. How did that go again? She thought about it for a minute, then stuck her foot in the stirrup and pulled herself up with a groan.

"Not bad," Ben smiled. "I promise you, we'll turn you into a real equestrian by the end of this week."

Charly gave him a tired smile.

"Forget it. I'll be satisfied when this horrible trail ride is over."

"Oh come on," said Ben after swinging himself up onto the other horse. "I'm sure it'll be a lot of fun. You'll see."

Before Charly had a chance to respond, the other riders set themselves in motion. Ben gave the lead line a tug.

"Come on, old boy, the others aren't going to wait for you."

Charly tightly gripped the side reins and bit her lower lip anxiously. Hopefully June was right about Björn not letting anything unnerve him.

Marty rode up front on a huge brown horse and chatted with the boy who was riding one of the small chestnuts. June sat on a white horse that pranced nervously behind her. Ben turned around in his saddle to look at her.

"Well now, does your Horse-Ferrari want to step on the gas again?" he called cheerily to her. "Nelson would like nothing better than to gallop all the time," he explained to Charly.

"How awful," Charly murmured.

"You think?" Ben laughed. "I think June likes it. You should see her when she jumps with Nelson."

"Jumps?" Charly croaked.

"Sure. Those two are training for a tournament. You should watch her sometime," Ben suggested. In a tone of respect he added, "June is really an excellent rider."

When June and her white horse rode alongside her a few feet away, Charly observed her out of the corner of her eye. Although she didn't know much about horses and riding, even she could see that the girl sat in her saddle as if she were meant to be there. How happy Charly's mother would be if she could ride like that.

Oh no! She couldn't get jealous now, too! Charly quickly looked away and concentrated on Björn's gray-white mane as it wobbled comically in time with his gait. In front of her, the twins rode, looking exactly alike right down to their hair. They talked to each other animatedly and burst into laughter periodically.

What would it be like to have siblings? At least then she wouldn't feel as alone as she did now. If she had a sister or a brother she could at least talk about how much her parents' separation hurt. How abandoned she felt. How unfair it was that no one asked her opinion, that in the end she was simply presented with a done deal. She certainly couldn't talk to her mother about things. She would say that everything was just a matter of time and that Charly would soon get used to the situation.

Sometimes she had the feeling that her mother didn't even want to know how she was doing. Maybe she was just afraid of the truth, because Charly had known for a long time that her mother wasn't always as cheery as she pretended. She noticed it just recently, when her mother thought she was alone and sat in the kitchen crying silently into a tissue.

"Charly? Charly!"

Charly looked up, startled. She hadn't noticed that Ben was speaking to her.

"Yes, what is it?"

"You aren't looking at the scenery at all," said Ben. "But you should – look at how beautiful it is here."

Charly looked around reluctantly. Ben wasn't exactly wrong. Today was a beautiful, clear day and she could see some imposing mountains off on the horizon. If Charly didn't know any better she'd swear that she was standing right in front of them. They were actually on a hilly meadow where beautiful flowers in every imaginable color grew. A narrow path led through the middle of the meadow, which they rode on in single file. Ben lengthened the lead so that Björn could walk behind the other horse. Bringing up the rear was June on her white horse, which was still prancing nervously. He was so light footed that Charly hardly heard his hooves on the soft earth.

After riding through the meadow, they reached a broad farm track and the riders fanned out again. Marty allowed herself to fall back with her big brown horse and asked Ben, "Everything okay here?"

"Couldn't be better," said Ben and smiled confidently at Charly. "Charly's really doing a great job."

"Do we really have to walk the entire time? It's totally boring."

Charly saw the boy ride over on the chestnut that had thrown him only yesterday. He gave Marty a challenging look.

"I want to gallop."

Marty took a deep breath, opened her mouth – and then closed it again. Whatever it was that she wanted to say to him, she decided to keep to herself instead.

"As I've been saying all along, we will not be galloping because we have a beginner with us," she said finally. Charly could hear how difficult it was for her to keep her cool.

"Well that's just great." The dark-haired boy rolled his eyes and groaned loudly. "First I have to make do with this mini-cold blood horse, and on top of that I'm only allowed to walk with him. Honestly, I expected this camp to be different. You should have written in your ad that Sunshine Farm is just for beginners."

"You'll have an opportunity to gallop," said Marty, "but not today. As long as Charly is along, we will stick to walking."

The dark-haired boy looked at Charly contemptuously. "Why didn't she just stay home?"

Charly turned beet red and stared desperately at the ground. The entire situation was terribly embarrassing for her. Although she thought the boy was being incredibly arrogant, he was right when it came to one thing: why did Marty insist that Charly go along? Especially since Charly would have liked nothing better than to stay behind at the farm.

"Then how about if the two of them walk all they

want and we go gallop a bit," the boy suggested. "Then we could wait for them to catch up."

Marty held the brown horse back a little more and considered the idea.

"That could work," she said finally.

"That, um, won't work," Ben said quickly.

"No?"

"Er, no."

"And why not?" Marty looked at Ben curiously. "Beyond the forest over there is a stretch for galloping. You could walk behind us at your own pace."

"Um, well, I wouldn't do that," said Ben and looked around helplessly.

Suddenly June turned up and rode close to her mother. Charly saw her whisper something quietly into her mother's ear. She would love to know what she was saying, but couldn't understand a single word.

"Okay then," Marty said finally. "Let's forget about that idea. It's simply too dangerous and that's that!"

"But I want to gallop," the dark-haired boy insisted. "What do the others think?"

"I think that wouldn't be bad," said the other boy, and the twin sisters nodded vigorously. "Oh yes, galloping. The trail is so nice here."

Charly would have liked nothing better than to turn invisible right there and then. She felt like a party pooper ruining everybody else's fun. It wasn't her fault that she didn't know how to ride.

"Well, I do have an idea," said Ben so loudly that everyone could hear him. "How about if I head back home with Charly? Then the others can gallop and everyone is happy."

"Yes, well, I don't really know. I don't really like the idea of you riding all alone," said Marty with hesitation. "Wouldn't I be breaching my responsibility of supervision?"

"Oh, you don't need to worry about that," Ben smiled. "Olaf and I will take good care of Charly and Björn. You can trust me completely. Isn't that right, June?"

June nodded.

"I think that's the best idea, Mom. Ben will make sure that nothing bad happens and the others get to do what they want, too. Nelson wouldn't mind a little galloping either. I have a feeling that he's about to explode."

"Alright," Marty sighed. "It doesn't look like we have any other choice. But you will be very careful, won't you Ben?"

"Sure thing, boss," Ben saluted her and turned his horse away from the group. Björn stomped slowly behind him. "Come on Charly, let's head on home."

Charly nodded happily. Anything to get away from there!

Chapter 13

"I should have known. Why did I let myself be persuaded to change my mind instead of doing what I thought was right?"

Marty, dirty and drenched in sweat, sat down on a bale of hay and took off her chaps. She tossed them down on the floor next to her, propped up her head in her hands and looked at June. "Sometimes I ask myself if this riding camp idea wasn't just pure stupidity. I feel like nothing is going right at the moment."

June stood with her back to the stable wall and said nothing. What could she say? She thought that the idea with the riding camp was, to put it mildly, not thought through well enough. Maybe it should have been planned a little more thoroughly beforehand, but that simply wasn't Marty's way of doing things. When she had an idea, then she had to make it happen immediately.

"Don't blame yourself," June said finally. "It could have been worse."

"Even worse?"

Marty stared at her with her huge eyes and brushed a strand of red hair out of her face.

"If I might remind you of what just happened, four campers fell off their horses, and as if that wasn't bad enough, the horses also had to run though Farmer Myers' field, of all places. If that wasn't really bad, then I don't know what is anymore."

June nodded. The trail ride was nothing less than a catastrophe. Although Marty said that everyone should gallop behind her at a controlled tempo, Navajo, Noel, Nino and Ninja dashed past Magister on the left and the right, bucking wildly, as if they were trying to qualify for the world rodeo championship.

Surprisingly, little Nano didn't join in and was well-behaved, riding behind Princess and Modena. Mark, Connor, Ronnie and Lila didn't have a chance with the crazy chestnuts, and one after another they landed on the soft dirt path. June chased after the Haflingers with Nelson and was horrified to discover them in Farmer Myers' canola field.

To make matters worse, just at that moment, the farmer happened to be in the adjacent field with his bulldog and saw the whole fiasco: how the Haflingers galloped through his field, how Marty and the others followed in a wild chase after the chestnuts, and how the horses continued to fool around before thundering through Farmer Myers' freshly mown meadow. They were finally bored enough to allow themselves to be caught, as if nothing had happened. Farmer Myers then got hopping mad and threatened Marty with the police and worse. June had no idea what he meant – what could be worse than that the police? The military? A special commando unit?

Actually, anything would have been all right with

her, if it meant finally teaching the wild Haflinger Gang some respect.

"It can't go on like this," sighed Marty and she got up from her hay bale, groaning. "I'll take a look to see how far along dinner is and then I'm going to take a bath. Everything hurts."

At least everything was working out well with the campers' meals during this first week. Mrs. Morris made a veggie casserole that tasted as delicious as it smelled. Dessert was vanilla ice cream and fresh strawberries. After dinner June felt much better and was amazed that most of the campers were still in good spirits. Except for Charly, who was once again sitting in front of her with a huge frown on her face, even though she really didn't have any reason to be so miserable. After all, she didn't fall off her horse!

Even Mark was in good spirits after getting to ride home on Magister instead of Navajo. He made such a big stink that Marty – reluctantly and gnashing her teeth – allowed him to ride the big brown horse while she got on Navajo.

"Can I ride the brown one for the rest of the week?" he asked her as dinner was cleared.

Marty shook her head.

"I'm afraid that's not possible, because I would have to ask his owner for permission first and he isn't here. He left him for me and I don't know if he would be okay with it if I allowed a camper on his back. What happened earlier was an exception because I didn't want Navajo to take off again."

A dark shadow came over Mark's face. "Then we can call him up."

"No, we can't. I don't want to disturb him when he's on vacation. Furthermore, he can't make an informed decision from a distance. He's never seen you ride before."

"Then I have to ride the Arabian after all," said Mark looking at June challengingly, "because I'm never ever getting on that horrible Haflinger again."

June was shocked and held her breath. She knew that Mark would try this again! But her mother would never allow that.

Or would she?

"I don't know," said Marty. "Nelson is June's horse and I can't just take him away from her. Aside from which, she needs to train for a tournament with him."

"Tournament?" Mark asked, his curiosity piqued. "What kind of a tournament?"

"June will be going to a jumping tournament with Nelson soon, and I promised to train with her."

"A jumping tournament?" Mark looked at June, clearly impressed. "How about that? This gets better all the time."

His gaze moved back to Marty.

"I don't care. As far as I'm concerned she can train with him as long as I get to have him for lessons and on trail rides. So, do I get him?"

Marty shook her head.

"No. That's impossible. Nelson is June's horse and she is the only person who rides him. If you're unwilling to ever sit on Navajo again, then we'll have to find another solution."

June breathed out a sigh of relief. Despite all the difficulties, her mother was keeping her promise and wouldn't allow Mark to ride Nelson. She'd watched the dark-haired boy ride and knew that while he wasn't a bad rider, he was extremely heavy handed. Although June knew that Navajo was very poorly behaved, she could also understand why he bucked his rider every chance he got. Simply the thought of someone tugging hard on the bit of her sensitive Anglo-Arabian made her hair stand on end!

Just as she got ready to stand and help the others clean up, Mark cornered her.

"You know, I will ride your Arabian," he whispered in her ear and smirked. "Just you wait and see."

June stood there with her plate in her hand and stared at him as he walked out of the kitchen.

"Are you okay?" Ben asked. "You look like you've just seen a ghost."

June told him what Mark had just said to her. Ben laughed contemptuously.

"What a big mouth. You don't have to be afraid of him, June. He's the kind of guy who spouts nonsense all day long and never manages to really accomplish anything."

"Do you really think so?"

June looked at him uncertainly. Her impression of Mark was that he was the kind of guy who knew exactly how to get what he wanted.

"Yes, I really think so. Come on, you can't let an idiot like that ruin your whole day."

Ben playfully poked her in the ribs and pushed her out of the kitchen.

"What do you think about asking the others if they'd like to have a game night with us? We could have a 'Trouble' tournament." Ben suggested.

"Good idea," said June. "At least that'll give us something else to think about. I'll go get our collection of board games."

She ran into the living room and pulled the box with the game out of the closet. Then she ran down the stairs and across the courtyard where Ben had already assembled the others under the big chestnut tree. June saw that everyone except Charly was there. She was probably back in bed with the blanket pulled up to her ears. Even Mark was there, much to June's surprise. She expected him to still be fuming over Marty not allowing him to ride Nelson.

Ben suggested that they play games of two against two until only two players were left at the end. Then the remaining players would play each other to determine the winner of the tournament.

"It'll be sudden death," he explained, "just like in the soccer World Cup, when the last sixteen teams play. And I will be the referee, so that everything is fair and above board."

He winked at June. She laughed. Ben truly was an all-around talent.

Everyone agreed to the rules and Ben divided up the players and decided who played against whom in each match.

The tournament kicked off with Lena against Carla. Lena never had the slightest chance and was trounced. Then Maxi and Ronnie played against each other. Maxi was luckier than her sister and at the last minute she was able to tear victory away from Ronnie. Next Connor and Mark competed against each other. June watched intently as Mark tried to provoke Connor again and again by saying that Connor couldn't possibly beat him. But Connor paid no attention and beat his opponent easily. June was happy for him. She liked the boy with the friendly smile. And of course she liked the fact that Mark didn't win. But she was surprised that Mark didn't get the slightest big angry. She could have sworn that he was the sore loser type, who couldn't lose a game without getting into a foul mood.

Then Ben called her and Hannah to the game table. It was a pretty even match although neither June nor the twin seemed motivated enough to win. When Hannah knocked out June's game piece shortly before she could bring it home, she just laughed.

"A little more fighting spirit, ladies," warned Ben. But neither June nor Hannah thought very much of that. They cackled and giggled as they knocked each other out until finally Hannah brought her game figures home. June congratulated her and got up so that Lila could take her place. Across from her, Jana sat down on the wooden bench. They played a very exciting match and Lila emerged as victor.

Ben divided up the winners of the respective games. Because there were five winners, Connor had to play twice because he was the only boy, once against Carla and once against Lila. He won both games. In the finale, he played against Hannah, who had won so resoundingly against Maxi. The others gathered all around the table and watched intently as Hannah and Connor waged battle against each other until Hannah finally won in a very close game.

"Congratulations to the World Champion of Trouble," called Ben and shook her hand. Then he gave Connor a friendly pat on the shoulder. "You weren't bad either, partner."

June laughed. Never in her life would she have guessed

that this day would end on such a pleasant note. She stayed
a while with the others, sitting under the chestnut tree and
enjoying the mild evening air. Maybe Marty's idea wasn't
so bad after all? Maybe a vacation camp like this was a
nice idea. When the sky got totally dark, the group slowly
dissipated. June packed up the game board and the figures
and tucked the box under her arm. The light was still on in
her mother's office upstairs. Didn't she say earlier that she
wanted to take a bath? June went into the house. Just as
she was about to go upstairs, she heard a door open. Marty
stood at the top of the stairs and looked down at her.

"June, do you have any idea where my wallet is?"

"Your wallet?"

June shook her head and went upstairs. The closer
she got to the top, the better she could see in the dim hall
light that her mother had dark circles under her eyes.

"It's gone," said Marty. "Just gone."

"It's gone? But that's not possible. Have you really
looked everywhere?"

Marty nodded. "I've already searched every corner of
this house."

"Where did you see it last?" asked June, trying to stay
calm. Her mother looked like she could burst into tears at
any second.

"In my office, in the desk drawer," said Marty. "And
it's not there anymore."

Marty sat down on the top step and wrapped her arms
around her knees. June thought that she looked like a
little girl sitting that way.

"Was there much in there?"

"Much?" Marty winced. "Only five hundred dollars
and all my credit cards. Let's just say, everything I have."

June gaped at her mother in disbelief. First the snaffle bit, and now the wallet. Her mother seemed to have nothing but rotten luck these days.

"And now?" she asked quietly.

"Now I call up the bank and cancel all my credit cards. I just hope that it isn't too late."

Chapter 14

"Next time tighten his front end, June. Otherwise he'll jump flat and may pull a rail."

Marty moved both poles in the blue-and-white oxer two holes higher.

"Come one more time."

June straightened her black helmet with the silver stripes that she'd gotten for her last birthday. She shortened the reins and transitioned into a gallop from a walk. Nelson's ears were pointed forward attentively and he increased his speed when he saw the obstacle in front of him. June sat back a little in the saddle.

"Hoho, old boy," she whispered. "You heard, we're not supposed to be as fast this time."

Three more strides. Two. One. And off! Nelson propelled himself powerfully off the ground with his haunches and flew in a high arc over the oxer. He landed on the other side, soft as butter, and galloped in broad strides across the field. June had to work hard to rein him in to a trot.

"Not bad," Marty called to her. "He didn't have any

problem at all without the height. That was definitely an L-Oxer. You just have to pay attention that he doesn't gain too much speed. If he starts to run, then his concentration suffers and he makes mistakes."

June removed the helmet from her head and shook out her dirty blonde hair. Was there anything better than flying over obstacles with Nelson? No way! Overjoyed, she leaned over her white horse's neck and cuddled her face into his silky soft mane.

"If it were my decision, I could go on forever."

Marty smiled and shook her head.

"You maybe, but not Nelson. He has to do most of the work, if I might remind you. Besides, you know that the best time to stop is when things are at their nicest."

She looked at her watch.

"Aside from which, I have to get ready. Bea will be here in half an hour."

Oh yes! June had almost forgotten Marty's plans for the evening. After the incident with the wallet last night, Marty's best friend, Bea, decided that Marty needed something to take her mind off of her troubles and invited her to a theater in DC. Mrs. Morris would be staying overnight at Sunshine Farm, so that the guests weren't without supervision. Lena and Maxi, who had stayed with Marty and June plenty of times, thought it was really funny that their mother was along for the sleepover this time. Fortunately there hadn't been any more unfortunate incidents during the past two days. Marty couldn't have handled it if there were. Although she had cancelled her credit cards in time, her five hundred dollars was still gone. Who could have stolen the wallet? If a burglar had been at the farm, then they would have robbed everyone else. No, that didn't really seem possible. Besides, Maxi, Lena and her mother were at the farm the entire time and would surely have noticed something. But that would mean that…June shuddered at the thought that someone on the farm could be the thief. Lost in thought, she walked off the field with Nelson on long reins.

"Hey, he can really jump."

June was so lost deep in thought that she didn't notice that Mark had approached her.

"If you had more horses like him, then this farm wouldn't be half bad. But with these nags over there…"

He looked contemptuously in the direction of the Haflinger Gang. The Haflingers were crowding at the paddock fence, waiting for Maxi and Lena to bring them fresh hay. June's face turned red with anger.

"You'd better take care not to let my mother hear you talking like that. You know perfectly well that she won't put up with people talked disparagingly about the horses."

"Oh, I'm just *so* afraid now."

Mark covered his mouth with his hand and acted as if he were terribly frightened. Then he laughed sarcastically.

"I don't care if your mother hears me talking this way. Unlike that strange girl, I'm not the least bit afraid of being sent home. She can go right ahead and call my mother to tell her to come and get me. What kind of a lame threat was that supposed to be – that I don't have to ride that horrible farm nag anymore?"

June had had almost enough.

"*That horrible farm nag* is smart for constantly throwing you," she said angrily. "The way you're always pulling at his bit – I'd throw you too! You have absolutely no sense for horses, and don't think for a minute that I'd let a bully like you ever sit on my horse."

Mark listened to her the whole time with a mocking smirk on his face. When she finished, he raised his eyebrows and looked at her as if to challenge her. "Are you really sure of that?"

"What do you mean, sure?" asked June, confused.

"That you won't let me on your horse."

June swallowed. This guy, with his overconfident attitude was kind of sinister. The word 'no' just didn't seem to exist for him. In fact, it seemed like the more she protested, the more he wanted to ride Nelson. If only this week were over and she could be with her friends, training for the tournament in peace.

"Yes, I'm completely sure," she finally managed to say and lightly squeezed Nelson's belly with her heels. And she was out of there. As she rode off, she heard Mark laughing behind her. *Never*, she swore to herself, *I will never allow you on my horse!*

She rode over to the hitching post where Nelson's halter was hanging and dismounted. She had to hurry. She and Ben had to muck out the open stable before dinner while Maxi and Lena took care of feeding. Marty looked so miserable the night before last that everyone was now trying to be extra-helpful and make life as easy as possible for her.

Everyone, of course, except for Mark, who was complaining as much as ever. And Charly, who moped around the farm with her sourpuss face, avoiding taking an interest in anything at all. Except, maybe, for little Nano, whom she sometimes visited at the fence. *Heaven only knows what was going in that girl's head*, June thought as she brought Nelson to his paddock. The white horse happily threw himself into the dust and then hurried over to his trough, where his protein mash was already waiting for him. June hung up his halter on the paddock gate and strolled over to Ben, who was already busily cleaning out around the Haflingers. The five chestnuts had already eaten and were now having fun inspecting the wheelbarrow full of manure and getting in Ben's way as much as possible.

"Come on, Nino, get out of the way."

Ben used his shoulder to shove aside the Haflinger with the long white mane, but in doing so he lost nearly half of the wet straw that he had just collected with his pitchfork.

"Now look what you've done."

Ben looked accusingly at the Haflinger, who was trying to get at his jeans with his broad soft mouth. Ben groaned and dug a treat out of his pocket.

"Okay, here you go, you old beggar."

"Do you have to reward him for his bad behavior?" asked June. "As if the Haflingers don't already make enough trouble for us."

"Oh, they're not really all that bad," said Ben dismissively. "I think that they were very well-behaved yesterday and today."

"Yesterday and maybe today, but the first riding lesson and the trail ride were just horrible. We can be thankful that none of the campers got hurt."

Ben massaged Navajo, who rested his heavy head on his shoulder, looking at June innocently.

"They aren't bad," Ben defended the chestnuts. "They're just, well, a little immature. A little more training certainly wouldn't have hurt them."

"You can say that again," sighed June. "But you know my mother, when she gets an idea…"

"Then she has to put it into action immediately," smiled Ben. "I know. And that's not really a bad trait, because just imagine what it would be like if your mother didn't do anything without thinking first."

June considered the question. It was true, what Ben just said. After her parents separated and the talk was that Marty would open a stable with June, all the relatives were up in arms. *Impractical and irresponsible*, they said. And most people probably saw it that way. Still, June was glad that her mother decided to take the leap, because as far as she was concerned, there was no nicer place in the world than Sunshine Farm!

"You're right," she said finally and grabbed the pitchfork that was leaning against the wall. "And now let's get to work and finish up here, because I'm starving!"

June and Ben cleaned up around the Haflingers at lightning speed and then raced toward the house with grumbling stomachs. They got there just in time to see Marty get into Bea's car.

"Wow, Mrs. Sunshyne, You look terrific," Ben called to her approvingly.

"Do you really think so?" Marty was flattered and giggled. She turned to June. "Can I really go like this?"

"Of course you can!" said June. "You look wonderful."

And she meant what she said. Marty was wearing a long, black form-fitting dress that was particularly flattering for her slim figure. Her normally wild red hair was combed neatly and artfully swept up in a chignon. June noticed that she even put on a little eye makeup.

"Marty!" Bea called to her. "Now get in the car or we'll be late."

"All right then." Marty smiled at June. "Just keep an eye on the place and make sure nobody does anything dumb, okay?"

"Don't worry," said June who smiled reassuringly. "We've got things under control, isn't that right, Ben?"

Ben nodded.

"You really don't have to worry, Mrs. Sunshyne. You just go to DC and have some fun. We'll take care of things here and see to it that everything is in order."

Marty smiled gratefully and got into Bea's car. Bea put the car in gear and drove off the farm. June and Ben watched the car until it disappeared around the curve. Then they went into the house. They almost bumped into Mrs. Morris, who was holding a pot of steaming potatoes.

"Oh good, you're here now. I was just about to call you. Do you have any idea where that dark-haired girl might be? Charly's her name, right?"

June shook her head.

"No idea. I haven't seen her in a while. She's probably just hanging out in the dairy kitchen, sulking. Should I go take a look?"

"Oh that would be nice of you, June."

"I'll come along," said Ben and walked out with her. On the doorstep they put on their working shoes again and walked over to the dairy kitchen. There was no one to be seen there. June started to turn around to walk back to the courtyard, but then something under Charly's bed caught her eye. Curious, she walked closer and bent down.

"I don't believe my eyes. Just take a look at this!"

Furious, she picked up her mother's wallet and held it up to show Ben. He stood there with his mouth hanging open and gaped.

"I-I-I'd never have expected that," he stammered. "Is everything still in there?" he stammered, shocked.

June took a look.

"Her ID and driver's license are here. Her credit cards, I think, are also all here. But the five hundred dollars are gone. Oh, wait till I get my hands on her!"

"June, just calm down first," Ben tried to talk her down. "Do you really believe that Charly stole the wallet?"

"Yes, who else could have done it? Or do you think it's just a coincidence that it's lying here under her bed?"

"But why would she have done something like that?" asked Ben. "Haven't you noticed what expensive clothes she wears? Her riding boots alone must have cost a fortune. I can't believe that Charly has any kind of money problems."

"How am I supposed to know why she did it?" said June, clearly annoyed. She simply couldn't understand why Ben constantly tried to protect Charly, even now when the evidence was so clear!

"Whatever. She stole it and that's got to be the meanest thing I can think of. And I'm sure she was also the one who cut through the snaffle bit. That evil creature – I knew all along that there was something strange about her. Maybe she had already stolen a lot of stuff and that's why she can afford the expensive clothes. Anyway, now she'll get her comeuppance!"

June stuffed the wallet in her pants pocket and turned to walk out to the courtyard. Suddenly she stopped dead in her tracks and stared at the figure in the doorway.

"Well look who we have here!" she said. "There you are. So I suppose you saw that we've found you out, huh? You lousy thief, stealing my mother's money. What did you do with it?"

Even in the dim light June could see that Charly was white as a sheet.

"Now open your mouth and talk. Where's the money?" June demanded.

Charly just stood there, not saying anything.

"June, please, now don't get so upset." Ben lay his hand on her shoulder to calm her and then asked Charly in a friendly voice, "Is there something you'd like to tell us, Charly?"

Charly acted like she didn't hear him.

"Start talking!" shouted June.

"Come on, June, that doesn't help the situation," said Ben comfortingly. "Your shouting doesn't make things any better. Why don't we wait until tomorrow, and then your mother can deal with it, okay?"

Although June didn't have the slightest desire to wait until tomorrow, Ben was probably right. Just then she was so furious that she could have easily lost control over herself and gone for Charly's throat. Maybe it really was better if her mother dealt with things tomorrow.

"Alright," she said finally through clenched teeth and allowed Ben to lead her out the door past Charly who still hadn't moved a muscle.

"And what are we going to do with her now?" she asked once they were outside in the courtyard.

"Nothing," said Ben. "We won't say a word to anyone until your mother gets back. Until then we'll act as if nothing happened."

113

"And what if she runs away before then?" asked June suspiciously.

"Runs away?" laughed Ben. "There's nothing here except fields and woods. Where could she possibly want to go?"

Chapter 15

Charly's heart beat so loudly that she felt like it could burst apart at any moment. She stood in the doorway long enough to realize that June believed that she'd stolen Marty's wallet. How ridiculous! She, Charly, a thief!?! Charly's legs suddenly felt as wobbly as jelly and her hands started to shake. As if she needed to steal money from that crazy woman!

But who could have put the wallet under her bed? Thoughts raced through her head. Was it maybe Ronnie, who slept in the bed over her? No, even if the girls in her room weren't exactly her friends, she couldn't imagine any one of them being a thief. Who could it have been?

Charly snorted contemptuously and sat down on the edge of the bed. It didn't matter who it was. Whoever it really was, June would lay the blame on her. And what then? Then Marty would call her father and request that he pick her up. He'd probably come immediately and pay back every last cent to be sure that nobody informed the police. Then he'd take her out to his house on the

Potomac, where she'd have to stay with him and his new girlfriend until the end of the week.

Charly angrily stomped her foot. No! No way would she go to her father. But what then? She stared thoughtfully at the small window and saw that the moon was slowly rising. She had to get away from here before Marty got back. The best thing would be for her to lie down in bed and act like she was already sound asleep. Then when the others were in bed and were really asleep, she could get up and sneak out of there. Then she'd have a few hours' head start to find a good place to hide. When her mother returned from London, she could call her on her cell phone and ask to be picked up.

Charly did some figuring. Her mother wouldn't be back for another three days. Until then she needed a place where she could sleep and get something to eat and drink. She decided to sneak into the house while the others were eating to get herself some food and drinks out of the pantry on the ground floor. She grabbed her backpack, went out to the courtyard and carefully looked around. Nobody there. She hurried to the house, taking long strides, quietly opened the door and slipped over to the pantry. She heard loud laughter coming from upstairs. Good, the others were still having dinner.

Working as quickly as possible, she tossed a few apples and pears into her backpack. Some fruit couldn't hurt. And what else? Charly looked around. Back there on the shelf were a few packages of cookies. Charly took three, some sliced bread, three orange juice packs and three bottles of water. She wrinkled her forehead as she noticed how heavy her backpack was getting. She couldn't pack too much or it would slow her down on her escape. She took along two packages of cold cuts and a salami from the top shelf and was just about to sneak out of the pantry when she heard footsteps on the stairs. Charly turned off the light and pulled the door closed from the inside. With her heart pounding she leaned tight against the wall and stood as still as possible.

"I'm just going to say goodnight to Princess," she heard a voice saying.

"Good idea. I'll come along and give Modena the apple I've been saving since before dinner."

"Oh yes, I'll give Princess an apple, too. Wait here while I go get one out of the pantry. Mrs. Morris said that we could help ourselves to one any time we want to."

Charly held her breath. She heard the steps come closer and waited for the door to open any second.

"Hey Jana, are you still hungry?"

Charly flinched. Of all people – June had to show up!

"Naw, I just wanted to get an apple for Princess and say goodnight to her."

The voice was directly in front of the door. The doorknob slowly started to turn and the door opened a slit to let a sliver of light from the hallway shine in.

"Why don't you give her a carrot out of the sack next to the stable door? We put them there especially for the horses."

"Oh that's even better. Let's get going. Hannah, what are you waiting for?"

The door closed again and Charly heard the steps going away. Once it was totally quiet outside, she slid her back down the wall and took a deep breath. That was a close call. Now she had to sneak out of the pantry without being discovered. She opened the door soundlessly and slipped through the hall when she heard the voices upstairs again. They sounded like the rest of the campers. Charly went to the door as quickly and quietly as possible, opened it carefully and hopped down the steps to the courtyard. A short time later, Mark passed her and gave her a dirty look. Charly acted like she had to tie her shoelace and waited until he passed by. Whew, that really was a close call!

She threw her backpack over one shoulder and walked across the yard as if nothing had happened. On the way to the dairy kitchen she passed Ronnie, Connor, Carla and Lila.

"Hey Charly," asked Ronnie in a friendly voice. "Weren't you hungry today? You didn't even come to dinner."

Charly shook her head.

"No, I feel a little queasy. I think I'm going to lie down and go to sleep. I'm sure I'll feel better tomorrow.

"Oh, I'm so sorry," said Ronnie sympathetically. "I'll ask the others not to make any noise when they go into the room later. Then you'll be able to sleep."

"Thanks," Charly mumbled and went into the dairy kitchen. She almost felt guilty for lying to Ronnie. The girl was always so friendly to her. At a different time and in a different place they probably could've become friends, but right now it was all about disappearing quickly before Marty could call her father.

In the dairy kitchen she hid her backpack carefully under her bed, took off her shoes and got under the covers with all her clothes on. It felt like an eternity before the others finally came into the room to go to sleep. She almost had to be careful not to fall asleep herself. When everything was finally dark and all the girls were in their beds and sleeping soundly, Charly got up and pulled her backpack out from under her bed as quietly as possible. Then she took her shoes and her windbreaker with one hand and her backpack with the other and tiptoed to the door in her socks. She turned the doorknob very, very slowly and pushed open the door. It squeaked a little, and Charly stood rooted to the spot for a few seconds before turning around. The girls were still sleeping soundly. Charly slipped out through the crack and closed the door. Then she went outside and breathed in the mild night air. Luckily it was a full moon so she didn't have to walk in the dark. Charly looked over to the big forest that bordered on the Sunshine Farm paddocks. She shuddered. At night it looked really scary. But on the other hand, the forest was better than the wide fields on the other side of the farm. The fields didn't look as scary, but they also wouldn't provide her with a cover.

Charly put her shoes on, tied her jacket around her waist and put on her backpack. When she finished, she turned and walked past the stables until she reached the paddocks. A short distance away she saw a few big, dark points that periodically moved. Suddenly she heard a very quiet, shy neighing. Actually, it was more like rumbling than neighing. She stopped and looked in the direction of the noise. The little chestnut stuck his head over the fence and quietly rumbled a little more. Charly went over to him and stroked his head.

"I'm sorry. I can't take care of you now. I have to get out of here quickly. Do you understand?"

The little chestnut looked at her with a friendly expression in his big dark eyes and rumbled again. Charly looked at him thoughtfully. Did he want to escape too?

After all, he was just as much of an outsider as she was and hadn't been accepted by anyone. Suddenly a jolt went through Charly. She went to the paddock gate, grabbed a halter and a rope and crawled under the fence. Then she racked her brain trying to remember how to put on the halter the way Ben had shown her. She awkwardly pulled it over the small chestnut's head. Charly wasn't sure if he was being patient with her or was just too surprised to react. At any rate, he didn't move from the spot and waited until Charly was finished. Then she fastened the rope to his halter and led him out of the gate to the courtyard. The chestnut followed her without hesitation.

Charly took a deep breath. She didn't know what got into her to make her take the horse off the paddock. Now she wouldn't just be accused of stealing money, she'd also be accused of horse theft!

This is getting better all the time, she thought darkly and scratched the little chestnut behind the ears. *What am I supposed to do now with you out here? And what will my parents think of me when they hear that I stole a horse?*

A dark smirk crossed her face. Let them think what they want. Had anyone shown her or this horse any amount of consideration? Why should she be the one to show consideration? And now, she was out of here!

She held the rope tighter and pulled on it gently. The little chestnut took a step toward her and rubbed his head on her arm. Charly was just about to head off with him when she suddenly heard a sound. It came from the direction of the strange building where the campers slept. She looked around frantically. It was too late to run away. Instead she leaned against the little chestnut and pushed him into the big shadows in front of the stable.

Charly stroked the chestnut's neck reassuringly and held her armed and squinted as tightly as possible to try to see better in the darkness. A tall, slim figure crossed the courtyard and headed straight for the stable where the white horse was kept, the one June was doing jumps with today. Charly saw the figure take a halter and a rope from the fence and then open the gate to the paddock. What could this possibly mean? She shrugged her shoulders. Who cares what it meant? It was all of no consequence to her since she'd decided to run away. Now the only thing that was important was to get away from the farm as fast as possible. She tugged again on the rope and then walked with the chestnut as quietly as possible around the house and alongside the paddocks over to the forest, which rose up ahead of her, looking dark and gloomy in the moonlight.

Chapter 16

A loud whinny penetrated the forest. All at once the earth began to quake. June stood in a clearing and heard a thundering sound that grew louder with every second. She turned slowly to the side and saw a huge herd of horses breaking out past the trees and they were galloping toward her. She stood there, unable to move, and observed the animals that were racing toward her with their nostrils flaring and manes flying. They came closer. Closer. And closer.

"Nelson!"

June sat up in bed with a jolt and looked around, confused. In the darkness she could see the outlines of the furniture in her room. She took a deep breath and wiped the sweat from her forehead. *A dream*, she thought, relieved. *It was just a dream*. For a moment she had actually believed that she was standing in the forest clearing, since it all seemed so real. June snuggled back under the covers, pulled her blanket to her chin and closed her eyes. She lay there happily dozing, when she suddenly heard a loud whinny. June jumped up. There really was a horse whinnying outside! That's why the dream had seemed so real. In a single movement she leapt to the window and tore open the curtains. She pressed her nose to the glass and stared down through the darkness. The farm looked so lonely and abandoned. June saw Bea's car in front of the door. Because the house was so quiet and not a single light was on, she guessed Bea was probably staying overnight as she often did. June hoped that her mother had had a nice evening and had recovered a bit from the stress of the past few days.

She thought for a minute. Should she go back to bed again or look around outside? She was absolutely certain that she heard a whinny. She sighed and took her washed-out jeans from a chair and pulled them on. She would much rather crawl under the warm blanket and get some more sleep, but on the other hard, she wouldn't be able to relax before she found out where the whinny came from. She quietly opened the doors and snuck down the hall to the living room where Ben, Maxi and Lena were sleeping. If she were honest with herself, then she had to admit that going outside all alone in the darkness was pretty creepy. Ben was in his sleeping bag on the carpet, while Maxi and Lena had gotten comfortable on the two sofas, sleeping deeply. Ben was the first to wake and look up at June, confused.

"Is it morning already?" he mumbled and looked out the window. "It's still dark outside."

"I know," whispered June, "but a horse outside whinnied."

"Are you sure? Maybe you just dreamed that."

"I'm totally sure," June insisted, "and I don't want to go outside alone. Can you come with me?"

Ben sighed. "If I really have to. I'm assuming you're not planning to give me a choice in the matter." He peeled himself awkwardly out of his sleeping bag.

"That's right," smiled June and waited for him. Just

as they were about to leave the room, they heard a loud yawn from behind them.

"What are you guys doing?"

Maxi sat up on the sofa and looked at them inquiringly.

June told her about the whinnying and that she and Ben wanted to see if there was anything out there.

"How exciting!" Maxi threw off the blanket and jumped up. "I'm coming along. We should wake up Lena too or she'll be mad that she missed out on something."

June waited impatiently until the two girls were finally ready to go. Then the four of them sneaked down the stairs and out to the courtyard.

"So, where do you think the whinnying came from?" Ben asked.

June shrugged her shoulders.

"No idea. I think we should just check around everywhere."

"Brrrr," said Maxi and huddled close to her sister. "It's totally spooky out here in the dark. I'm not going into the stable alone. Who knows what's waiting for us there."

"Don't be silly," said June, "What would be waiting for us? But if that's the way you want it, then we'll all stick together."

Even if June would never admit it, she was secretly happy to have her friends with her. Maxi was right; the farm did look creepy in the dark. For a minute she thought about whether they should wake up her mother or not, but decided against it just as quickly. Why should she worry her mother unnecessarily? Maybe she was just mistaken and there really was nothing wrong.

At first that seemed to be the case. Björn, Olaf, and

Magister stood in the open stable, dozing with their heads hanging, and everything was fine with Princess and Modena as well. June looked around. Nelson should be around her somewhere, but she couldn't see him anywhere despite the fact that the white horse should be especially easy to make out in the darkness. Could he have gone out on the paddock? June went outside. No. Anyway, she clearly remembered closing the entrance to the paddock last night so that the horses wouldn't eat too much of the fresh grass. She looked in every nook and cranny, but the white horse was nowhere to be seen.

"Nelson is gone!" she called.

Ben, Maxi and Lena looked at her in shock.

"Are you sure?" asked Maxi.

"Completely sure. Where else could he be?"

Although they knew that it made no sense, the four of them looked around for him one more time without success. The Anglo-Arabian really was missing!

"Then he was the one that whinnied," Ben said finally. "But where could he be? Do you think there's a hole in the fence anywhere?"

They walked along the fence and checked every last link and post, but couldn't find anything out of the ordinary. When they got to the gate, June shrieked.

"His halter is missing! That means someone stole him! We have to go look for him!"

Ben rested a hand on her shoulder to calm her down.

"Now wait a minute, June. Maybe there's another explanation. Besides, what direction would we go to follow him? We don't even know where to go."

June stomped her foot angrily.

"We have to do something. Nelson is gone, do you

125

understand? Who knows where they might take him. I'm going to get my mother, to tell her to call the police."

Without waiting for an answer, she turned around and slipped under the fence when they suddenly heard a shrill whinny resound across the courtyard. June, Ben, Maxi and Lena looked at each other and then raced off in the direction of the sound as if on command. They came to a stop in front of the Haflinger Gang's paddock and then looked around.

"Now what?" asked Ben. "Where do we go now?"

They heard another whinny and this time it came directly from the paddock. June was the first one under the fence, and she raced across the sandy paddock to the open stable where she expected the chestnuts to be. Maybe the horse thief was still there and was trying to steal one of the Haflingers.

Suddenly she ran into something big and warm and she bounced back, landing right on her bottom in the sand. She saw a huge head with long hair standing above her.

"Navajo!" she called, surprised. "What are you doing here?"

The ringleader of the Haflinger Gang walked around nervously, whinnying loudly.

"I have no idea." Ben reached his hand out to June and pulled her to her feet.

"At any rate, he's totally nervous. Something must be upsetting him."

Navajo wasn't the only one that was nervous. June noticed that Nino, Ninja and Noel were also standing around along the back fence of the paddock snorting nervously, with their ears alert and their eyes looking toward the forest.

"There's something over there." Ben squinted and tried to make out something in the darkness. "But what?"

"The thief!" said June. "It must be the thief who's taking Nelson away right this very minute."

"In the forest? Why would he take him into the forest?" Ben wrinkled his forehead.

"Wouldn't it be more likely for him to come with a horse trailer, rather than running off on foot?"

"Who knows? Maybe he has an accomplice waiting for him with a horse trailer on the road behind the forest," said June. "We've got to go after him as quickly as possible."

"I don't know." Ben scratched his head thoughtfully. "Wouldn't it be better if we informed the police, as you just said?"

"We don't have any time for that!" June was so agitated that she practically screamed at Ben. "By that time, the thief could already be miles away. Do you have any idea how many stolen horses are never returned to their owners? Come on, we have to follow them!"

"But on foot we're much too slow." Ben still wasn't convinced. "If we take the dirt path to the woods and don't see anyone, then that means that the thief is already in the woods. And by the time we get there, he really will be miles away."

"Then we just have to ride!" exclaimed June.

"Hey, do any of you have an idea where Nano might be?" Lena asked suddenly. "I haven't been able to find him anywhere."

June and Ben gaped at her with their jaws hanging open.

"Lena is right," Maxi interjected. "Nano really is missing. We've looked everywhere for him."

"Then he's been stolen, too!" June yelled. "Now let's finally get going, otherwise the thief really will get away!"

"And who is going to ride which horse?" Ben asked with hesitation.

"You could take Björn," suggests Lena. "I'll take Olaf, and…"

"I have a better idea," June interrupted. "We'll take the Haflingers."

"The Haflingers?"

Lena stared at her with her mouth hanging wide open.

"You want to take the Haflingers out in the open in the dark? Who knows what they'll do in the middle of the night when they already get into so much trouble by daylight?"

"But the Haflingers know where Nelson and Nano are," insisted June. "Just look at how agitated they are because their buddy is missing. They'll definitely lead us to the thief."

"June is right," said Ben. "The Haflingers have always been together and they'll definitely search for Nano. And wherever Nano is, that's where we'll find Nelson. So come on, people, let's take a chance!"

They quietly slipped into the saddle room and got out saddles for the four remaining Haflingers. In the darkness it wasn't exactly easy to find the right snaffles and saddles, but June wanted to avoid turning on a light at all costs. They'd be discovered soon enough, but it was too late for explanations. Now they had to find Nelson and Nano as quickly as possible. June just hoped it wasn't too late!

Chapter 17

Charly stopped for a moment in front of the dark forest and had trouble swallowing the lump that had built up in her throat. The tips of the giant pines ahead of her stretched high into the sky and waved noisily in the wind. Charly stared through the trees, but in the darkness she couldn't make out much of anything. She had been counting on its being relatively easy to see by the light of the full moon. She looked up to the sky in bewilderment. She hadn't noticed that in the meantime, dark clouds had blown in and settled implacably in front of the moon. She was also pretty sure that it wasn't this windy earlier. And on top of all that, she saw a bright flash of lightning light up the sky ahead, and the first raindrops began to fall. Charly would have liked nothing better than to turn around, but she had no other choice. If she didn't want to be discovered, then she had to risk moving onward.

"Come," she said hoarsely and pulled the little chestnut behind her into the woods. She was extremely happy that she had taken him along, because if she had been all alone in the darkness, she would have been much more afraid. After they had walked for a few minutes and reached a small clearing, she stopped and looked around. Had she really just heard a sound or had she imagined it? She huddled closer to the little chestnut and listened. No, she hadn't imagined it, there really was something! It was a thudding noise that sounded like something very big walking on the soft ground, although walking wasn't exactly the right word. Running was more like it. In fact, Charly had the feeling that the noise was getting closer quickly. Very quickly, in fact. And then it seemed like everything happened at once.

First she heard a loud bolt of thunder and lightning flashes so bright that the woods seemed to be illuminated for a moment by a glaring spotlight. Then Charly heard a loud scream and, shortly thereafter, she saw a white horse blazing through the trees, its eyes rolling and its nostrils flared, galloping past her at an insane tempo. Although there was no rider sitting on it, it did have a saddle and a snaffle on. The stirrups banged against its belly and that seemed to provoke him even more. Before Charly could take it all in, the ghostly apparition passed by her and disappeared behind the trees.

The little chestnut, which all this time had been standing completely still next to her, started to prance and snort nervously.

"Relax, little one," said Charly, and she lay a hand on his soft nose.

The gelding calmed down immediately and nuzzled her with his strong head.

"Come, let's get going again," said Charly. "We have to stand under the trees somewhere."

It had started to rain and it didn't take long before it

was pouring buckets on them. With their heads down, Charly and the little chestnut on the rope walked across the clearing and back into the forest where the rain was coming down considerably less intensely. Charly brushed a wet strand of hair out of her face and leaned on the gelding. What kind of a horse could that have been? Somehow it seemed familiar to Charly, but on the other hand, not really. She shook her head. Better not give it too much thought or her feelings of anxiety would increase. It was eerie enough in the woods as it was.

But as if the first experience weren't enough, Charly suddenly heard a loud scream. Aghast, she pressed herself against a damp tree trunk and peered between the trees in the direction of the clearing. Since there was no lightning and the moon was still hidden behind the clouds, in the pouring rain and darkness she could only make out the outline of a big figure making its way through the trees to the clearing. Charly held her breath. A horse! Could the white horse have returned? Suddenly the little chestnut next to her began stepping in place. Then he lifted his head up high and let out a shrill whinny.

"Shhh!" Charly whispered.

Too late. The horse in the clearing heard him and whinnied back. Charly knew that the best thing for her to do would be to run away. But she just stood there like a pillar of salt and looked at the horse on which, she was now able to discern, a rider was sitting. Suddenly, lightning flashed again and a loud clap of thunder filled the air. The horse reared up on its back legs and kicked at the air with its front hooves. It looked even spookier than it did earlier when it galloped through the forest without any rider.

"Owww!"

Charly flinched. The scream sounded anything but spooky. She rubbed her eyes and saw how the horse, this time without a rider, landed its front hooves on the ground again and then galloped off as quickly as it possibly could. What should she do now? Run away. But the cry of pain sounded so earthly and real that she had to go take a look. She held onto the little chestnut's rope even tighter than before because he was still quite nervous. She then carefully walked between the trees to the clearing. As she got close enough, she saw someone lying on the ground next to the trees. Charly went a little closer.

"Charly? What are you doing here?"

Charly was startled and stayed rooted to the spot. She was prepared for just about anything – except seeing June lying there and asking her reproachfully what she was doing in the woods.

"You know," she mumbled and approached June. "I could ask you exactly the same thing."

June sat up with some difficulty. Pain crossed her face and she grabbed on to her shoulder.

"I'm searching for the horse thief who…"

Suddenly her jaw dropped and she stared past Charly to Nano, who was standing closely behind the girl.

"Nano! Where did you find him?"

She looked at Charly suspiciously.

"Don't tell me you're the person who stole the horses?"

June tried to get to her feet, but groaned and sat down again.

"Owww. Darn it, this really hurts like crazy. I just hope I didn't break anything."

"Maybe you should just sit here and wait until I bring

133

help," suggested Charly. You didn't have to be a doctor to see that June was in terrible pain.

"Ben, Maxi and Lena are still somewhere here in the woods," groaned June. "If you find them, one of you could ride home and get help."

"And what should I do with him?"

Charly gestured to the little chestnut with her head.

"The best thing is to take him with you and he'll lead you to the others, just like Navajo led me to him, although I was actually on Nelson's trail."

Nelson's trail? Charly shook her head. She had no idea what June was talking about, but she saw that the girl desperately needed help. She took the little chestnut and went in the direction that June had just come from. She didn't need to wait very long. Suddenly the gelding at her side got agitated and whinnied again. Shortly thereafter, a second whinny came from nearby and got louder and louder. Before long, Ben and the girls from the farm were standing in front of her. One of the girls held a horse on a rope, which Charly thought was the chestnut that June just fell from.

"Charly? What are you doing here?"

Ben looked at her with his eyes wide open.

"I'll explain that later. One of you has to ride quickly to the farm and tell someone that June is hurt."

"Hurt!?" Ben said, shocked. "Where is she? We were worried about her when we found Navajo without a rider."

"In the clearing over there. I think she broke something. The best thing to do would be if someone got an ambulance right away."

Ben took a deep breath and turned to Maxi and Lena.

135

"You two ride to the farm together. That's safer than just one of you heading over. I'll go with Charly to June."

Maxi and Lena nodded, turned their horses and slowly trotted off between the trees. Ben dismounted, pulled his horse's reins over its neck and walked in silence with Charly to the clearing. When he saw June lying there, he broke into a run and pulled the chestnut behind him.

"June!"

"Ben!"

June sat up, groaning and looked at him with relief.

"So Charly found you."

"Well, to be honest, he found Nano, not me," Charly said, pointing to Nano and scratching her behind the ears. "There sure seem to be all sorts of horses running around in the forest tonight."

Ben and June look at her with big eyes.

"What do you mean by that?" asked Ben excitedly. "All sorts of horses in the forest?"

Charly told him about the white horse she saw earlier, that was galloping through the clearing without any rider.

"Nelson!" June shouted and groaned again from the pain. "Ben, please, we have to find him."

Ben put his hand on her good shoulder to reassure her and thought for a moment.

"Which direction did you see him go?"

Charly motioned with her hand to the spot where the white horse had disappeared between the trees.

"Okay, you stay here with June and I'll go after Nelson."

Without waiting for an answer, Ben swung himself up onto the chestnut and galloped off across the clearing. Charly and June watched him go until he too disappeared

136

between the trees. Once he was gone, June gave Charly a questioning look.

"Now why don't you tell me what you're doing here with Nano? We thought that a horse thief had made off with him."

"And you figure if someone steals money, she's also a horse thief?" Charly asked tersely.

"Well, you do have to admit it's weird that first we discover the wallet under your bed and then find you here in the forest with Nano."

Charly's expression darkened. There was a long moment of silence. Then she looked June right in the face.

"Do you really think I'm so stupid that I would steal something and then leave it under my own bed?"

June bit her lower lip and considered this.

"Maybe you're right," she said finally. "Probably no one who steals a wallet would just leave it lying around in the open. But then explain to me what you're doing with Nano in the forest in the middle of the night."

Charly avoided her gaze and lowered her head.

"Could it be that you wanted to run away?" asked June quietly.

Charly felt her eyes tear up and turned self-consciously away from June.

"Why did you want to run away?" asked June quietly. "Were you afraid that my mother would call the police?"

Now there was no holding back. Charly let her tears flow freely and, sobbing, threw herself against the little chestnut that was standing there, solid as a rock. He didn't move an inch from the spot as she pressed her face into his mane.

"I – was – so – afraid – that – my – father – would –

come – get – me," sobbed Charly, and she clutched the little chestnut even tighter.

"Your father?" asked June, taken aback. "Why don't you want him to pick you up? I thought all along that you wanted to leave Sunshine Farm as quickly as possible."

Charly shook her head.

"No, I'd rather stay at Sunshine Farm than have to go stay with my father. I don't want to have anything to do with him ever again."

"But why not?" asked June, and she groaned again. "Ow, I have to stop moving."

Charly turned around and looked at her.

"You don't understand – my parents just got separated."

June laughed bitterly.

"Oh yeah? To be honest, I understand a whole lot about that. When did your parents separate?"

"In April."

"That's not long ago at all," said June sympathetically. "Then it really does still hurt a lot. My parents have been apart for more than a year, and even if you don't believe me, you do get used to it."

Charly felt like someone had hit her in the head. She had never thought about why June and Marty lived at Sunshine Farm without any man. She was always too busy thinking about her own problems.

"But my father already has a new girlfriend," she then said quietly.

June sighed.

"I know that hurts. I was really miserable when I found out that my father had a girlfriend, too. But believe me, it gets better as time goes by."

Charly looked at June, scrutinizing her.

"Aren't you still angry with him?"

June sighed.

"Sometimes I am still, but I've learned to accept him and his new life. You can't be mad at your father forever. I'll bet that he loves you as much as he always did. Once you understand that, it's not nearly as bad."

Charly looked at her uncertainly. Could June be right that the time would come when she wouldn't be angry with her father?

"You can believe me," said June, as if she were reading her thoughts. "And Nelson really helped me a lot. He was always there for me when I needed a friend." A sad expression crossed her face. "I just hope that nothing bad's happened to him."

Just as Charly was about to say something to comfort her, she heard loud voices in the forest. Then a frightened whinny. Nano grew uneasy again and stomped nervously in place. Charly and June give each other a frightened look. Minutes passed without anything at all happening.

"Get going now! Forward!" someone at the other end of the clearing suddenly shouted. In the meantime, the electrical storm had blown over and it was slowly turning to morning. Charly saw Ben leading the white horse with one hand and pushing a tall, slim figure with the other. Charly held her breath. It was the boy with the dark hair! What was his name again? Oh yeah, Mark.

"Nelson!" June called out and sat up, groaning. "How is he? Did he get hurt?"

"I think he's just fine," said Ben. "And so's our horse thief here, too, although he doesn't deserve it. He only got a few scratches when he fell," said Ben. "He might have gotten a few more since then, when I was trying to *convince* him to come along with me."

Ben's smile spoke volumes.

"After I rode for a while in the direction of the television tower, I first found Nelson, who had gotten his reins tangled up in a bush. Then when I was riding back with him on the rope, I saw our thief here, who was limping along. It looked like the fast Arabian was a little too fast for this blowhard."

Ben looked at Mark contemptuously. Mark was looking at the ground with an angry expression on his face and Charly noticed that he had a dark red gash on his forehead.

"But that's not nearly all: look at what fell out of our hero's pocket during our little, ahem, altercation."

Ben waved a few bills triumphantly in the air.

"The five hundred dollars!" shouted June. "Does that mean he's the one who stole the money?"

"Not only that," said Ben, "I'm sure he was the one who stashed the wallet under Charly's bed so that we'd suspect her."

"What a dirty dog!" groaned June. "And where did you leave Noel?"

"I had to tie him to a tree, because I needed a free hand for our blowhard," explained Ben. "I just hope that he doesn't pull it out by the roots. I'll go back and get him as soon as the ambulance arrives and takes June and Mark away."

As if on cue, they heard a siren in the distance as the day broke.

"Thank goodness," groaned June, "I couldn't have taken the pain for much longer."

Chapter 18

"What a shame that the week is over already. I would love to stay here longer."

June looked at Charly and smiled.

"Well, look at you – a few days ago I thought that you wanted to turn around and go home immediately."

Charly laughed.

"Yes, well, a few days ago I thought I was afraid of horses. If I had known what nice animals they are…I would have started riding them a long time ago."

"I couldn't believe my eyes when I suddenly saw you standing there in the forest with Nano," said June. "I never would've believed you could do that."

"Me neither," answered Charly earnestly. "I can't describe it, but when he saw I was running away, Nano looked at me in such a special way. Somehow I had the feeling that we belong together. I felt sorry for him all along because no one wanted him, and although the other Haflingers like him, he's still the outsider. That's the way I felt when my parents got separated."

"I know," sighed June. "And he behaves so much better than his buddies do. Who would've thought that a…" she swallowed what she was about to say.

"You mean that a beginner like me could ride him?" asked Charly. "You're right, I am a beginner. But something about Nano made me trust him. Maybe that's why it works so well with us."

"Could be," said June, and she clumsily leaned back in her wicker chair, which Marty had positioned under the big chestnut tree. While her broken shoulder didn't hurt anymore, the cast limited her movements considerably. Again, she thought back to the night in the forest when she and Navajo separated from the others to ride after the shadow that turned out to be Mark and Nelson. Although Navajo was afraid to ride alone in the dark, he dutifully followed Nelson at first. But when he got to the clearing and heard Nano's whinny, it was all over. Instead of following June's command to gallop after the white horse, he panicked and reared up. June hadn't expected that at all, and fell off his back to the ground, and wound up with a complicated shoulder fracture.

"So tell me, are you very disappointed that you won't be able to participate in the tournament?" Charly asked June.

June wrinkled her forehead and thought for a moment. "A little, I guess," she said finally. "But there'll be other tournaments."

"I'm just so sorry," said Charly. "Somehow I feel like it's my fault that you can't participate."

"You?" June looked at her, surprised. "Why do you think that?"

"Well, If I hadn't taken Nano along, then the other Haflingers wouldn't have whinnied and you wouldn't have woken up and wouldn't have ridden Navajo and…"

"Wouldn't, wouldn't, wouldn't," said June, and she

waved her good arm around. "Just think for a minute – if I hadn't woken up then I wouldn't have been able to follow Mark and Nelson. Who knew what else Mark might have done with him and what might have happened if Ben hadn't found Nelson so quickly? In fact, I owe you my gratitude for the whole thing." She smiled at Charly. "Besides, it was incredibly dumb of me to accuse you of stealing the wallet. I'm really very sorry."

"Forget about it," said Charly. "I didn't behave particularly well myself. Do you have any idea why your mother didn't file a complaint with the police against Mark?"

"I think that she felt sorry for Mark's mother. The poor woman was obviously overwhelmed by that son of hers, since her husband was constantly away on business trips and she had to deal with him by herself. And she hinted that this wasn't the first time something like that happened. At any rate, she replaced the snaffle and we already found the five hundred dollars."

Charly held her hand up to her forehead to shade her eyes from the brightly shining sun, allowing her gaze to wander.

"I wonder when the others will return from their trail ride." She sighed. "I know that it's still much too early for this, but next time I'm definitely going along when the other campers go on trail rides."

June frowned suddenly and looked at her sadly.

"I don't think that there will be a next time."

"What?" Charly asked, disappointed. "What is that supposed to mean – you don't think there will be a next time?"

"I think my mother understands now that she took on more than she could handle with the riding camp. We just don't have the means to do it. Although the Haflingers haven't behaved too badly these the last days – that's not including Navajo's fit in the clearing – they just aren't trained well enough to use for formal riding lessons. And we can't afford to buy new horses. The rooms for the campers also have to be fixed up better, but we don't have the money for that, either. Mrs. Morris was kind enough to help out with the cooking this week, but I have no idea what we'll do without her." She winked at Charly. "My mother, you see, is a pretty lousy cook."

"What'll happen with the Haflingers?" asked Charly. "What are you going to do with Nano?"

June shrugged her shoulders.

"No idea. We'll probably hold on to them for a while longer, but in the long run, of course, it's very expensive to keep so many horses." She put her good hand on Charly's shoulder reassuringly. "Don't worry, when we do give them up we'll definitely see to it that they're in good hands. And as long as Nano is out here, you can come by any weekend to visit him. It's not all that far away from Washington."

Charly nodded and sighed deeply. On the one hand, she sympathized with Marty, but on the other hand, it made her terribly sad to think that now that she finally felt at home here, Sunshine Farm wouldn't be a riding camp anymore. She turned her head to look over at the Haflinger paddock where Nano was grazing peacefully. He seemed to be enjoying the fact that he had it all to himself. Because Mark was no longer there, Connor now rode Navajo and Ronnie, who originally rode on Nano, rode Noel.

Charly looked fondly at Nano. She hoped that Marty

would find a good home for him. Just as she started to get up and go over to him, she heard a car pull up in the driveway. Was someone already being picked up? Marty and the other campers weren't even back from their trail ride yet. She checked her watch. She'd probably be the last to get picked up from Sunshine Farm since her mother's flight wouldn't be landing at Dulles Airport until sometime in the evening. Just then, a big dark blue BMW drove around the corner. Charly couldn't believe her eyes. Her father! What was he doing here?

Chapter 19

From where she was sitting under the chestnut tree, June observed how Charly slowly approached the BMW that parked in front of the entrance to the house. A tall blonde man got out and hugged Charly. June could see that she resisted him at first, but then returned the hug. June smiled. She remembered only too well the first few times she saw her father again after her parents' separation. Then Charly took a step back and told her father something and gesticulated wildly with her hands. Then she walked ahead of him and brought him to Nano, who was curious and came to the fence as soon as he heard Charly's voice. June still found it fascinating how the shy little chestnut and the melancholy girl with the black hair fit together. It reminded her a little bit of her own relationship to Nelson.

Without him she wouldn't have managed to get through the difficult time after her parent's separation nearly as well as she did. She looked over to Nelson's paddock, where he was standing near the fence and waiting for the other horses to finally come back from their trail ride. He couldn't fathom why he had to stay home all the time now and he always gave June a surprised look when she brought him back to his open stable after grooming him. Suddenly Nelson threw his head back, ran excitedly back and forth along the fence and whinnied loudly. June didn't even have to look to know that the others were returning from their trail ride. She smiled. Patience had never been one of Nelson's virtues.

Now she spied the group. Marty was on Magister, leading the way into the yard. June got up with difficulty and went over to them. Ben brought Björn to a stop in front of her and jumped out of the saddle.

"Hey, is somebody here already?"

He motioned with his head toward the big blue BMW parked in front of the house.

June nodded.

"Charly's father arrived. I suppose it won't be very long before all the other parents come by to pick up their kids either."

She sighed.

"It's too bad, actually, that they'll all be gone again. I really got used to all the action on the farm. I'm sure it'll be horribly boring when everybody's gone."

Ben grimaced and nodded.

"You're right, I like it a lot better when there's a whole lot going on. What do you think – is there a chance your mother will change her mind?"

June shook her head.

"I doubt it. And she's right. We don't have enough money to start up a real riding camp."

June went back to her chair under the chestnut tree

and watched Charly and her father go over to Marty. Charly's father shook her hand and said something to her.

Marty looked around and called Lena, who had just brought Olaf to the back, over to her. June watched her mother put Magister's reins in the girl's hands and then walked over to Nano's paddock with Charly and Charly's father. The entire time, Marty conversed animatedly with Mr. Schultz. Every so often June could hear her loud laugh resonate across the courtyard. She wondered what the two of them had to say to each other.

Finally, after all the horses were put away, Marty, Mr. Schultz and Charly walked over to June under the chestnut tree. Charly walked in front and was beaming from ear to ear.

"June! June! This is my dad. He's picking me up because my mother's flight was delayed."

She plunked herself down on the bench in front of June and put both her hands on June's knees.

"We absolutely have to tell you something! Just imagine, we…"

"Let's start from the beginning," Mr. Schultz interrupted his daughter. "And don't you think June should get the news from her mother?"

Charly nodded reluctantly.

"Okay, if that's the way it has to be. But hurry up, Marty. I feel like I'm going to explode from excitement!"

June looked from her mother to Charly to Mr. Schultz and back again. They sure were keeping up the suspense! Marty sat down next to her daughter and put her arm around her waist.

"June, hon, you're not going to believe this, but Mr. Schultz just made me an unbelievable offer."

"An offer?" June asked and gaped at Charly's father with her eyes wide open. "What kind of an offer?"

"Mr. Schultz made me an offer," said Marty joyfully, "to become my business partner."

"Business partner?" June repeated with astonishment. "What's that supposed to mean?"

"Oh come on, June, don't you understand?" Charly burst in. She was so excited that she couldn't hold back anymore. "My father will be a business partner in Sunshine Farm, which means he'll invest in the operation while you and your mom still run the show."

She turned around to her father. "Did I put that the right way?"

"More or less," he laughed. "After Charly told me what a great place this is, I thought that I needed something to invest my money in."

"Invest?"

It was still all Greek to June.

"It's like this," explained Marty. "Mr. Schultz takes a financial stake in Sunshine Farm, so that we can finish renovating the dairy kitchen and buy new horses. Uh, better trained ones than we have right now." She looked over at the four Haflingers that had just gotten back from their trail ride and were now doing mad imitations of whirling dervishes because they had to be hosed down. "Our fellows, uh, need a little more time than I had originally expected," Marty smiled angelically. "Just think, June, we could even hire someone to do the cooking."

June stared at her mother with wide eyes.

"Are you trying to tell me," she finally began, "that we're going to have a riding camp after all?"

"Of course that's what we're saying!" shouted Charly and jumped up and down excitedly in front of her.

"And you haven't even heard the best part yet. Because my dad is now a partner in Sunshine Farm, that means I can come as often as I want. I'll come every vacation and as often as possible on the weekends. Isn't that terrific?"

June nodded enthusiastically. After her night in the forest with Charly, she had become extremely fond of the dark-haired girl. You could almost say that they'd gotten to be true friends in the last few days.

"I know who you'll be riding then," smiled June.

"Me, too." Charly looked at her meaningfully. "My horse, of course."

"Your – horse?" June was completely confused. When will they stop with all the strange hints?

"Well, Nano, of course!" exclaims Charly. "Dad said he'll buy him for me!"

She threw her arms around June and hugged her as well as she could with the cast in the way.

"I also need a friend who's always there for me," she whispered in June's ear. "Just like you have Nelson."

"Nano will stay here at Sunshine Farm," added Marty. "And you and I will take care of him when Charly isn't here."

"Wow, that's nothing but good news!" June exclaimed enthusiastically.

"Not just," said Marty carefully. "I still have a not-so-good bit of news for you."

"And that would be?" June looked at her mother with trepidation. What could she be talking about?

"Well, as soon as you're back on your feet, we'll have a lot of work to do. The Haflingers have to continue to be trained and we have to try out some new horses, a few rooms have to be painted, and, and, and…"

June laughed.

"That's fine with me, as long as we've got Sunshine Farm. I can't wait to find out who our next guests will be…"